NATURAL POUL

My original hen—the foundation of the strain

NATURAL POULTRY - KEEPING

JIM WORTHINGTON

Crosby Lockwood Staples   London

Granada Publishing Limited
First published in Great Britain 1964 with
the title 'Poultry Keeping Simplified' by Faber & Faber Ltd
Revised and republished 1970 by Crosby Lockwood & Son Ltd
Reprinted 1974, 1975 & 1976 (twice) by Crosby Lockwood Staples
Frogmore St Albans Herts and 3 Upper James Street London W1R 4BP

ISBN 0 258 96813 3

Printed in Great Britain by Fletcher & Son Ltd, Norwich

CONTENTS

To the Long-suffering Hen

LIST OF ILLUSTRATIONS

The line drawings are by
the author's daughter,
Linda Mary

PREFACE

'What is good is not new: What is new is not good.' So said a German statesman, subsequently liquidated, of the Third Reich. And that, briefly, is what I think about the present state of poultry-keeping as an industry. Largely it is based on big business.

There are, however, thousands who actually like poultry, who like to make and mend, to do for themselves. In the process they make many mistakes and incur losses, at a time—if they are pensioners—when time is scarce and money is not too plentiful.

This little work is intended for newcomers, particularly those who want nutritious eggs and healthy hens, naturally raised. Left to their own guidance, they will very probably perpetrate most of the usual mistakes. Many—some deliberately—I have committed myself. In the process good chickens and hens have suffered—for which I beg their pardon. I promise to refrain from repetition.

I have learnt the hard way, mistrusting on principle what is written as either hearsay or propaganda, misleading and confusing at best, positively dangerous at worst. Poultry-keeping is not an abstract science requiring elaborate equipment and higher mathematics. Poultry are living beings, individuals; not very bright, not very sensitive, and not made for sadistic experiments and mutilation. They are not laboratory animals, they are livestock. And in my submission they are best and most easily kept on the good earth.

I have been taken to task, yes, by friendly critics too, for advocating a system that, if generally adopted, would require the use of some 600,000 acres of grass. If indeed I had the temerity to preach to the majority I could retort that most if not all of the 600,000 acres would be all the better for judicious stocking by 60,000,000 hens. Actually I have endeavoured to counter the propaganda by interested parties in favour of the existing techniques of controlled environment, multiple battery cages, complex extravagant feeding stuffs and all the ballyhoo of modern poultry "farming". Farming, my foot—as much like an agriculturists idea of farming as Dachau was to a holiday camp. Modern poultry plants also need incinerators to cope with the carcases.

Admittedly, the occasional bird does die even under my system. When it happens I give myself a black mark for not anticipating it, and present the cadaver to a local gamekeeper; his ferrets aren't fussy, nor are greyhounds. But, after very many years experience first and second hand, I know which system is safer, and some Vets agree with me. One, in my presence, after describing the precautions he takes to exclude infections from his laboratory birds prophesied that the time would come when there would be only two systems of poultry keeping, the super hygienic such as his, and J. W's. Yet this very same authority, a personal friend of long standing, refused to test the efficacy of greenfood as a coccidiostat on the grounds that as he did not know the chemical analysis of greenstuff he could not compound a similar ration for the experimental control. Worse, between us, we had finished a bottle of my Armagnac, to no purpose!

It is this matter of greenery that I cannot sufficiently overstress, even to the necessity of growing it. In this respect given good management, grass is so much easier to grow and to feed. But grass is not vital for rearing good chickens, nor for producing first class eggs. GREENFOOD IS. Knowing this I can confidently advocate the use of a suitably designed intensive house for the poultry keeper with the minimum of land, *providing he gives his birds what they miss by being kept inside,* viz, fresh air, sunlight, earth, exercise and greens at the rate of at least 2 oz wet weight per day. One lettuce a week will not do.

Assuming that our budding egg producer has no more than a quarter acre he has the choice of keeping 25 birds outside versus two or three or even four times that number inside, making use of the manure to grow successive crops of succulents. This unpleasant by-product need be no problem even in a built up area if kept covered and dry. Even better if composted. Otherwise it can be a headache to neighbours and a source of reproof from the Local Authority, for one hen produces 1 cwt per annum; and it all stinks. Even with as little as one quarter acre he may find room to rear some replacement pullets.

Even this is not obligatory. Between the wars I used to buy from a gamekeeper ex-broody hens at 2/6d. apiece. Many I sold back to him next Spring at 5/-, a very lucrative transaction. Meantime they had produced a gratifying number of big eggs. They were isolated from the rest of the flock in night arks and covered scratching sheds; no artificial lighting. I know a farmer who finds that battery soiled hybrids lay quite sizeable eggs in their second year, by which time they had for the most part finished dying from fowl paralysis, at any rate. He buys them for a little over killing price from a breeding establishment and gets his money back the following Spring, by selling them as ovenready boiling fowl. In his case he has installed electric light.

From this you will gather that the man who wants to produce eggs with the minimum trouble is not bound to read the rest of this book. For myself I practice what I preach. I hate buying eggs—that is why my pullet eggs go into waterglass to tide over the late Autumn shortage. Before doing so I tap them against another egg to test the strength of the shell.

One other way of obtaining revenue is to breed for blue and/or blue red hackle feathers. Fly fishers are avid for them, especially from Old English Game Bantam cocks. It is a messy business removing the neck skin and does not appeal to me. On the other hand it can be a lucrative means of cashing in on surplus males. And of course Bantams eat considerably less than large fowl. The victims must be at least 18 months old by which time they will have eaten materially into the eventual profit. Even so £5 a time is not to be sneezed at.

Chapter 1

EGG PRODUCTION

The urge to keep poultry, even in these days of ready-made counter-attractions, is a constant source of surprise to one who has spent the greater part of his life in an advisory capacity. There is no dearth of recruits. Some of them have the same effect on me as the Duke of Wellington's raw levies had on him—positively frightening.

Naïve and gullible, they are easy meat for the slick salesman. If only one could get at them before they commit themselves. If only they would listen to advice from someone with nothing to sell. If only . . . but then, this is the age of advertisement and propaganda. The voice of one crying in the wilderness cannot be of much avail; though that is no reason for silence.

To some of these would-be poultry tycoons the loss of a few hundred pounds—or a few thousand for that matter—is not of much consequence; their pride is more affected than their pockets. It comes as something of a shock to learn that success in their own profession or business is no guarantee of a worthwhile return on their capital expenditure; that their estimates can be so adversely affected by perverse poultrymen, power cuts, poor stock and unforeseen contingencies. They pay dearly for their fun; let us hope they obtain some satisfaction by telling the world that there is no money in poultry.

That of course is just as untrue as the belief that any fool can earn a good living from hens. It is true that certain exceptionally able men have made a lot of money from poultry-keepers, but they would have done equally well in other spheres. Newcomers must not expect to make a fortune from hens and their produce.

Yet they can supplement their incomes quite materially so long as they are able to do the daily chores, are in a position to cut their feeding costs, and to obtain retail prices for their wares.

There is too the hobby aspect. One hears of men who, on retirement, just break up for lack of employment. How much more sensible to utilize their new-found freedom to advantage. Some have already committed themselves, for better or worse, to poultry-keeping.

I believe that many, unfortunately, have chosen badly and spent unwisely, to the greater profit of the manufacturers of broiler, deep litter and battery houses, and the producers of misbegotten mongrels. With the increase of intensivism quality has suffered. With lower quality it is only reasonable to expect lower prices. As a result of lower prices producers have increased their numbers and invested in more mechanism in the hopes of maintaining their incomes, thus further aggravating the situation.

Now this sort of thing may be, for the time being, not too unprofitable for the wealthy businessman who takes up egg production in a big way. And there is nothing that you and I can do about it. It is just as impossible to restrain these people from keeping poultry as it is to restrain the farmer's wife and the smallholder who have always kept chickens and always will; irrespective of whether they are or are not profitable. That kind of competition has to be faced both at home and abroad.

Just why specialist egg producers in this country should expect to make a good living out of what for the most part in most countries is regarded as an incidental by-product, is difficult to understand. The continental peasant does not expect his fowls to pay so handsomely as to justify specialist labour, nor does he leave his fowls to the tender mercies of a hireling, as so often happens in this country. He realizes that livestock does not thrive on neglect, that of all species of domestic animals hens in large numbers are the trickiest and most vulnerable to mismanagement. That is why he or some member of his family assumes responsibility. The hired man, if there is one, may assist; but the hens are not expected to carry his or anyone else's labour charges.

2

Here, on the other hand, they have on their backs the additional weight of the food merchant, the hatchery, the packing station, the manufacturers of drugs, antibiotics and hormones, the veterinarian, and the veritable horde of experts, some experienced, some even altruistic. It is indeed a heavy burden, and not surprising that they break down. Yet this is the accepted order, someone else's stock, housing, food, over the cost of which the poultry-keeper has little or no control. And even less over the price he can obtain for his produce. What sort of basis is this for a profitable business—to buy retail and sell wholesale?

Compare this with the state of affairs pre-war when a man bred his own stock, reared it himself, compounded his own rations, made his own houses, and in many cases did his own marketing, either retail direct or, in the local markets, on the strength of the quality of his produce. To this day there are poultry-keepers who have never fallen for the fetish of super-specialization. So far as is practicable they have retained for themselves all the profits at every stage, day-old, point of lay and disposal. They even make logical use of the manure or sell it to advantage. The day when one could hope to make a profit from other people's ready-made pullets, even if they are healthier than normal, selling them a year or less later at a time when everyone else is doing the same, is over. If therefore the would-be poultry-keeper proposes to emulate the crowd, he has been warned; for the majority is not always right.

It follows then that some alternative must be propounded. If, as most customers agree, the modern technique has failed to provide them with a palatable breakfast egg, the obvious solution is to return to the traditional. Admittedly many pre-war practitioners made a sorry mess of keeping poultry extensively; but it was because they failed to realize that there are rules of Good Husbandry which must be obeyed. The most important commandment is 'Thou shalt not overcrowd'.

There are two reasons, one pathological—a hen's biggest enemy is another hen—the other nutritional: the certain way to ruin a pasture is by overstocking. Grass needs a rest, therefore

3

grazing must be controlled. It helps if other stock can be employed
to turn a surplus into milk or beef, but it is not essential. For that
matter grass is not essential either, but for the greater part of the
year access to it is the most convenient way of administering what
I regard as the ingredient most responsible for quality, in eggs or
stock. Raw greenfood is the foundation of health. The failure to
provide it has caused the deterioration of the modern hen and the
commercial egg. Our continental rivals know this and, unlike the
lazy English, take steps to provide it.

No two persons' circumstances are alike. Some are relatively
well off and can afford to buy their experience. They have
perhaps already made up their minds exactly what they are going
to do, whose houses, batteries, brooders and chicks they will buy.
They have worked out their potential income, possibly from
published accounts laboriously compiled from statistics collected
several years ago. (There is inevitably a time lag in such literature.)
Meantime prices have changed. What the most successful made a
couple of years ago does not necessarily bear any relation to what
they, complete novices, are likely to make next year. Besides, in
the nature of things, the information given to the economist is con-
fidential. Worse, it may be inaccurate. At best it cannot be very
comprehensive; space forbids. For instance the source of the
stock is not normally disclosed. And the success of any venture in
livestock is more dependent upon its quality than upon any other
single factor. Advertisements are no guide. The value of personal
recommendation is related to the altruism of the person. In general
it is safer to buy locally from someone who has a reputation,
whose methods have stood the test of time.

Time, I agree, is of some moment. When one has reached the
age of sixty-five one has none too much to spare. The temptation
to go ahead is strong. It must be resisted. There is little profit
from pullets costing 25s. each, fed on complex extravagant food,
sold the next summer at less than half their cost, even if they are
all or nearly all alive—which is highly problematical. Not all
pullets cost 25s. Some, mass produced, reared like broilers, are
obtainable in large numbers for as little as 16s. each. The quality

of such stock varies; the degree of selection, if any, is dependant upon the skill, experience and honesty of the person who crates them. *Caveat emptor.* Some, genuine selected point-of-lay pullets, may cost 30s. or more. In the Home Counties pure-bred Marans for instance have changed hands at 45s. apiece. If the house is acquired on hire purchase, so much the worse. If it is large, badly designed and not too well made, its second-hand value is not going to augment the estate appreciably. Nor will it prove much of an attraction to the next owner of the property. Even should all go marvellously well it will take several years to recoup the purchase price.

That is no way to start—if the venture is expected to be remunerative. Better to buy second-hand, both live and dead stock, with the guidance of someone who knows the value of both. Better still to buy day-old chicks and learn how to rear them. The experience will be valuable or salutary or both, and not so costly. At least the depreciation of the birds will be less. It will surprise the novice to know that this item in the cost of production of eggs is second only to food. Next comes labour—if one is sufficiently fortunate as to obtain any.

If however the size of the flock is restricted to, say, two hundred, and most of the eggs can be sold retail, the venture should prove to be reasonably profitable and by no means too arduous. Anyone reasonably active should take a flock of this size in his stride—given a sensibly designed house. And from that category I exclude the normal deep-litter house. Instead I would recommend an open-fronted shed divided into two compartments, at the back a slatted or weld-mesh roost—not perches and thin wire netting—no wider than 3 ft, so that one can comfortably handle the birds at night. The back should of course be solid except for a gap of, say, 2 in at the eaves, baffled by vertical barge boards or a generous overhang of the roof; the front preferably of ½-in wire netting fixed to an extension of the roof or a hood, sloping backwards to the top of the litter board at an angle of 20°. This effectively keeps out the rain and slows down the wind. Preferably the house should face south. This way the litter will stay dry and the atmosphere not unpleasant.

As to the roof, there are three alternatives, lean-to, three-quarter-span or pent-roof. The latter most readily lends itself to other purposes but requires more framework and more skill. The lean-to type is more economical to build. It provides head room where it is needed, over the path of the attendant. The same applies to the three-quarter-span design. Gutters are of course required fore and aft, whereas the lean-to needs but one. For sheer economy therefore much can be said in its favour. On dry, well-drained land a polebarn structure and an earth floor will do. It is perhaps not widely known that a concrete floor can cost half the price of the house.

The choice of roofing material is restricted, in order of preference, to corrugated asbestos, iron or aluminium. Of these three iron sheets need maintenance, the others do not. Asbestos requires the heaviest framework, has the lowest second-hand value, and is the most vulnerable when dismantled. It may be asked, why consider this aspect? For the very good reason that poultry-keepers unlike old solidiers, are very mortal. Farmers in particular become quite excited when bidding for second-hand sheets. If I were a rich man I would plump for aluminium. A word of caution however—one should use aluminium nails, screws or bolts.

For framework there is an alternative to timber: metal angles, slotted and drilled, or second-hand scaffolding. For cladding there is much to be said in favour of exterior hardboard, or resin-bonded exterior plywood. In each case screws, not nails, must be used with wooden framework; or very soon the material will part company.

Such a structure should be less than half as costly as the orthodox house. There is no need for insulation or mechanical ventilation. These frills may be necessary to make litter 'work'. The real function of a house is to keep poultry in health, not to provide the right conditions for making compost. The two requirements clash violently. There is no way of reconciling them. In any case it is better practice to provide manure trays and clean them weekly, or dropping-pits to be emptied yearly, than to allow the birds to foul their litter and to eat their own ordure. To spend hours raking and forking during the winter, and moistening it in summer to keep down the dung-impregnated dust, does not impress me as labour-saving.

The dimensions suggested for 200 layers are 50–60 ft long, 16 ft wide. The nests can be fitted below the manure trays with flaps opening forward for egg collection. If a manure pit is preferred, the slatted roosts can be built at the back of the house so that the dung falls outside, in which case concrete slabs on the earth are desirable. In a bleak situation it may be advisable to fit a hinged flap, or detachable screen. If it is more convenient to have the pits inside they should be ventilated at either end at least 6 in below the slats. In either case a different location will have to be found for the nests. They are best sited parallel with the roosts, if dry mash is fed, on top of the food hoppers, forming a corridor in which the birds can be rounded up for culling. An intelligent craftsman can have fun making his own furniture. The less resourceful may prefer to buy hoppers and nests and distribute them all over the place. It is surely more labour-saving to have them in a straight line. With a little ingenuity one can install an overhead trolley for food distribution and egg collection.

As for watering devices, the choice is legion, some costly and reliable, many merely costly. A pig trough placed outside the house, accessible to the birds via vertical spars 2 in apart, has much to commend it. In bad weather it can be boxed in and heated if need be by an oil-lamp or immersion heater. It is a simple matter to fit a ball valve. If, as frequently happens, this should fail, the house is not flooded.

Some may query the necessity for a partition. Other folk have flocks of hundreds, nay thousands. My answer to that is a question—how do they catch them? How for that matter do they see the halt or the blind? In practice they don't. That is one reason why small flocks do better than large. Even the most argumentative agree on that. I know from my own experience how well a dozen will lay, how two lots of twenty-five can be expected to beat fifty, just as two separate hundreds will almost certainly

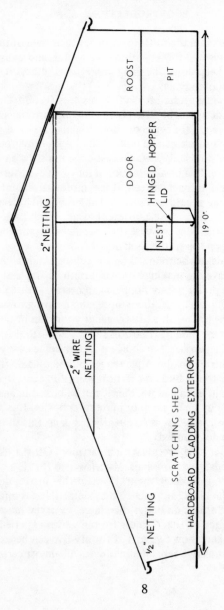

FIG. 1. Dry-litter house—4 square feet per bird

8

produce more eggs than two hundred. There is another reason too why a partition is justified. At the end of the laying season about half the flock is worth retaining for at least a second winter, under artificial light, of course. Only one hundred replacements are necessary.

It would in profile be ¾ span 25 ft x 19 ft, providing head room where it is needed for the attendant, who on entry at one end would have the slatted manure pit on his right hand, on his left a door giving access to the scratching shed, uncluttered with furniture. This door would normally be open. Beyond the door would be the food hoppers providing 22 ft of feeding space for the 100 fowls, plus 3 ft for grit and shell hoppers hanging from the door. Above the hoppers I would have the nests, all 22 ft of them, the nest floor some 2 ft high, that is at a lower level than the slatted roost which is 3 ft from the ground. From the top of the nests there would be wire netting to the roof. Thus the corridor would provide a catching area and the attendant could do his chores without deviating. If I had many of these houses I would fit an overhead trolley for food distribution and egg collection and of course water would be laid on.

Manure removal could be easily mechanised via the quickly detachable end of the house. The slats on wire netting or better still weldmesh would be hinged or slotted. The food hoppers would be surmounted by the nest-alighting board. The nests could be either communal or individual to choice. From the roof of the nest there would be more wire netting to prevent unauthorised squatting.

At either end from 4 ft upwards, and the whole of the front I would have half inch netting. The roof would have a generous overhang. There might be need for glass preferably in the roof, but I rather doubt it. So much for the house, how about the material?

Corrugated sheets, with their high second hand value, about £1 per sheet? Some 70 would be required. Aluminium sheets. Too expensive. Similarly plastic sheets. Exterior hardboard? I think so; estimated requirements, 8 ft X 4 ft, 25 at most. As for the framework I have more than a sneaking regard for slotted angle, galvanised of course; alternatively cedar 2 in × 2 in and 2 in × 1 in. At this stage please do not ask me 'How much?' What I visualise eventually is a 'Do it yourself poultry house'.

So much for the specialist egg producer with no further ambitions, who is unable to provide his layers with the minimum area of land viz. 100 birds per acre (The text books recommended 200 per acre—may they be forgiven). As to how many units of 100 he proposes to keep he must bear in mind that a hen produces manure at the rate of around 1 cwt per year, and that this unpleasant substance must be kept dry and free from rats.

He may, by judicious mixing with peat moss, for instance, persuade market gardeners to take it away, even perhaps to pay for it. He could maybe, for all I know to the contrary, succeed in making first class compost by dropping peat or straw through the slatted roost. The point I am trying to make is that he must not ignore this disgusting commodity. And the best of all solutions is to dig or plough it in for the growing of vegetable crops to feed back to the fowls and save part, a very important part, of the feed bill. If there is any to spare, put it on the blackcurrants; they love it.

To revert to the semi-intensive house. Since I first propounded the idea I have given it further thought. To my real regret I have not had an opportunity of testing it with a full complement of fowls but I would have no hesitation in advocating it for the man who cannot let his birds outside.

From slotted angle and alloy, ply or hardboard, one can construct a range house for a hundred layers. The frame dimensions are 9 ft long, 8 ft wide, requiring 120 ft of material. For cladding the requirements are five 10-ft sheets of corrugated alloy, mounted horizontally, giving 6 in of overlap; and less than three sheets of ply or hardboard for nests and ends. The floor can be of slats or weld mesh. Mounted on *broad* skids, it can easily be towed, even on heavy sticky land.

For that rapidly disappearing 'FREE RANGE' producer with his hundred or multiples and 'DO IT YOURSELF' ideas I can

FIG. 2. Metal range house

confidently recommend the metal-framed mobile house shown above.

There is nothing difficult in rearing day-olds, given good equipment and the realization that for the first week draughts are fatal; and that from three weeks of age the youngsters need progressively more room and more ventilation. The best of all brooders is a good hen. Half a dozen will comfortably raise 100 chicks. Next best is the contact heat 'electric hen', or, if electricity is not available a modified warm-floor brooder with an open front to the hot chamber, a canopy just clear of the chicks' backs, and a manure tray between lamp and chick—a paraffin-impregnated bedroom is not to be recommended. At three weeks one can safely remove the heat. The canopy, lifted a little, will

11

provide enough comfort, the open front will encourage rapid feathering. At six weeks many will be sleeping on top. If the chicks are reared in a shed two straw bales on their sides, up against the wall with a sack sagging between, held by bricks, will serve just as well as a more pretentious hay box.

Should he have a larger garden or a paddock his scope for economies is wider. The chicks can be reared outdoors, certainly from the age of three weeks. He has the choice of night arks or range shelters. Either type can be fitted with nests and scratching-sheds. They can be used for both rearing and laying purposes. In winter they can be raised from the ground and the manure removed from below when necessary. A range shelter of 9 ft by 8 ft fitted with a slatted or weldmesh roost can comfortably sleep a hundred birds. This, plus a low shed of corrugated iron—painted for aesthetic reasons—400 sq ft in area, will give just as good results as an expensive deep-litter house. To provide a structure 8 ft high for a bird not more than 18 in tall is absurd. When will people realize the winter production is due to artificial lighting, not to windowless houses, wire floors or battery cages?

As for these latter, I regard them as an insult to a good pullet. A few are useful as a means of identifying the layers of poor-quality eggs and those not laying at all; or for holding surplus hens till a customer arrives. For anyone selling eggs direct they are best kept out of sight. Many customers have very strong views about cages and the quality of the eggs therefrom. As a matter of fact battery eggs are just as good as any others if the occupants are provided with greenfood and earth and sunshine. But that, save on a back-yard scale, is out of the question. For anyone other than the partially incapacitated, or as a means of learning the art of culling, I regard them as uneconomic, by no means labour-saving and, in some circumstances quite nauseating. Let those in a built-up area seriously contemplating the system consider the disposal of that nastiest of all by-products, battery hen manure; and flies.

Finally, a word about marketing.

For thirty years eggs have been controlled in some degree, rationed, subsidised or supported. Now at last one can sell where one likes—even to the Packing Station, though in one case I know eggs have to be delivered there. The subsidy is being gradually reduced, the Egg Marketing Board is on the way out, and prosecutions for selling unstamped eggs to shopkeepers are just a memory. One may perhaps look forward to a return to the auction market and maybe an extension of the Womens' Institute activities in this respect, for there is an insatiable demand for good eggs on the part of the discriminating customer, who is sick and tired of the sight of white yolks, of shells that crack when boiled, tasteless and unappetising, sad and grey in colour. The affluent society is only too willing to pay what I personally regard as a ridiculous price for genuine brown eggs that fill their prewar sized egg cups. Many motorists are only too pleased to travel miles to acquire them. True, not every producer likes to have his weekend ruined by garrulous customers who never have the right change. There are alternatives.

One Packing Station I know offers a premium for bona-fide grassfed eggs. A smallholder on the edge of a residential area finds it more profitable to collect and retail eggs than to produce them. Wholefood and Health Food shops, the Farm and Food Society and the Henry Doubleday Foundation are avid for more supplies. The Soil Association sends its eggs by train to Baker Street. In short now is the time for more good eggs and more satisfied customers. And I have a feeling that as the mass producers realise that they can make more profit from fewer birds by returning to the Laws of Good Poultry Husbandry they will dispense with their sophisticated machinery in favour of simpler and safer techniques.

Not every one agrees that my sort of egg tastes better than what I have heard referred to as 'the plastic egg'. One highly intelligent customer I know was convinced that her eggs were genuine because there was a wisp of dirty straw in the carton! Some customers actually prefer mild eggs: but not my clients. For breakfast they must have yellow yolks and flavour.

This matter of quality remains a matter of contention. In an effort to resolve it, panels of well-known personalities have been assembled, blindfolded and given eggs to eat. They have failed to differentiate significantly between free range and intensive eggs. It is not stated what are their qualifications as tasters. Dare one suggest that middle-aged pipe smokers with vitiated palates are not ideal for the task? They should be replaced by children, preferably non-smokers and teetotallers. The mouths of babes and sucklings. . .

Finally and of real importance I strongly recommend the use of an electric candling device such as the 'Ovolux'. Its powerful concentrated beam shines through the egg even the brownest and thickest shell, showing up hair cracks, meat spots and bloodspots. It is, agreed, a chore if one has a large flock but if you have ever knocked the top off a boiled egg and found it full of nastiness you will appreciate the desirability of protecting your customer from such a shock; and your reputation from her clacking tongue.

Chapter 2

BROILERS, DUCKS, TURKEYS, REARING REPLACEMENTS

Broilers have been attractive. A house can be purchased for the price of a field officer's gratuity. Many have been. Just how profitable they have proved, their owners should know by now.

Quite apart from the more publicized and controversial aspects, siting and rating of houses, taste—or lack of it—there are inherent dangers in any form of mono-culture. If it is allied to or dependent upon big business, so much the more dangerous; as has already become obvious across the Atlantic. There, so one gathers, all forms of meat are sold in supermarkets. They dictate the price. There is ruthless competition between the breeders. If the primary purchase and the ultimate sale prices are dictated by monopolists, what chance has the processor?

The quality of the original importations varied, but careful selection has resulted in more uniformity, so much so that many birds are of excellent conformation, more especially the females. Egg production, in some strains, leaves much to be desired. Sooner or later such stock will need boosting with what the geneticist calls additive genes. In a later chapter the way to take advantage of this situation is indicated. This aspect apart, I do not regard broiler production as suitable for the novice. Even allowing for the very heavy capital out-lay, who wants to become, in effect, a chicken-minder for some vast concern? There are more satisfying means of supplementing one's income.

At the moment some producers of broiler hatching eggs are finding it reasonably profitable. But it is distinctly precarious. No hatchery will, understandably, give a firm contract. The stock is provided by the hatchery, sometimes reared by them or their agents. Thus the buyer's profits depend on someone else's skill in

15

breeding and rearing. There is no redress, no appeal. And not everyone relishes the prospect of regularly rounding up thousands of pullets for bloodtesting and vaccination—a most unpleasant procedure on a hot day in a dusty deep-litter house.

Broilers are not the only form of table poultry. There is an impression that as they become cheaper they bring down the price of other poultry meat. Not everybody thinks they are of such good value as, for instance, boiling fowls. Broilers have, however, one very real advantage—they are oven-ready. To the busy or lazy or squeamish this makes all the difference between a purchase and a search for something equally easy to prepare and cook; maybe out of a tin. Where boilers are available as attractively presented as broilers they should hold their own; in their favour they have flavour.

Duckling production has possibilities. Capital requirements are relatively low, housing and fencing especially. Not so food and litter. To raise ducklings without an assured outlet is not to be recommended. For packing stationers and butchers are not interested in odd lots. And there is no time margin—they are either ripe or out of condition. If they are not marketed when fully feathered they lose weight and plumage immediately. The opportunity of making a profit has gone.

Even so, by direct sale to restaurants well-bred Aylesburys can be profitable. It is of course essential to prepare them for table. Not everyone likes killing and plucking. I hate the idea of both. Ducks are, on the one hand, so trusting, and on the other, so adequately covered with feathers and down, that the idea of either appals.

There is no point in producing duck eggs for the packing stations. Some confectioners are prepared to pay reasonable prices. In the right circumstances the cost of production can be low. Given a stream and plenty of range, ducks can survive on the minimum of bought food. They will in fact consume no more than hens. In such conditions the cost of fertile eggs will be little more. The obvious next step is to produce day-old ducklings. That will require an incubator or more. The choice of cabinet machines is restricted to those that accommodate the eggs on their sides; not on their ends as with hen eggs. Let someone else kill and pluck them.

Turkeys? The very idea terrifies the novice. Yet it need not. Given a few acres or a simple shed, turkey poults can be reared with no more trouble than chicks, with similar equipment but twice as much of it. There is of course the risk of blackhead but, in my experience, given a plentiful supply of greenfood, it is no more to be feared than coccidiosis in chickens. There is still money to be made out of turkeys, purchased at about ten weeks of age, a modest profit can be made, more especially if some home-grown food is available. One producer of my acquaintance grows kale on one side of his turkey shelter and oats on the other. What is left, very little incidentally, is ploughed in and the alternative crop sown next spring. The turkeys adjust their own balance between greenfood and cereal.

Finally, chick-rearing for sale to egg producers is in some localities, the Home Counties for instance, well worth consideration. It requires some experience, a relatively small amount of capital, and a little patience. One cannot expect to gain a reputation immediately. Provision will have to be made for retaining a large proportion for laying; the first sales must be regarded as advertisement. The next year should result in an increased demand. As with other commodities, quality speaks for itself.

The first step is to obtain or construct reliable equipment, the next to contact a breeder of real repute. He, or she, may easily have more demands for eight-week or older pullets than can be met. In some cases chicks can be reared on contract. The breeder may have his own ideas on the type of brooder, but the most critical is unlikely to cavil at a well-designed 100-chick-size brooder-fold, with chicks outside on good short grass at three weeks old. Till then heat can be provided by oil, calor-gas or electricity. After that the chicks can provide their own, under a blanket canopy. A covered wire run attached to the brooder protects them from crows and magpies. If they are moved every second day there is no risk of coccidiosis. At eight weeks they should be allowed to range. Such chicks compare more than

17

FIG. 3. Night ark—front—adapted for brooding

favourably with the mass-produced variety and can very soon earn for themselves a reputation for hardiness. There is more profit to be made from this transaction by the rearer than by the customer unless he is very favourably circumstanced. Yet not all of these are in a position to rear their own. The farmer with a milk-round for instance is only too anxious to obtain reliable pullets at a reasonable price. The success of such a rearing venture depends on the breeding of the raw material, the chicks.

How is the novice to know which of the highly-publicized hybrids to purchase? Let him take the advice of someone with wider experience. In many years I have found no reason to doubt the wisdom of recommending breeders who long ago gave up the practice of introducing other folks' cockerels; whose flocks are closed. From such the likelihood of obtaining paralytic progeny is

18

reasonably remote. First-cross chicks from two such breeds can be expected to give uniform and consistent results.

These various alternatives are suggested for the poultry-keeper with some capital and some experience. I know of no method of increasing one's income without both. Whether one selects ducklings, turkeys, or chicks, the choice of housing need cause no headaches. Two types, the open-fronted and range houses previously described, are eminently suitable for ducks and turkeys. For brooding young stock, chicks, poults or ducklings, I can recommend a modified night-ark, accommodating a brooder, capable of being attached to a folding chassis, all of my own design.

The alternatives suggested in the previous pages are possibilities for the right person in the right circumstances. They are all capable of providing a modest income from a modest outlay in a relatively short time. The more ambitious or needy will be tempted to double or treble his stock; that will require more capital outlay, maybe additional labour. Personal supervision will be more difficult. Quality will suffer. The law of diminishing returns will almost certainly begin to operate; more especially when the owner lacks experience.

There are two ways of making a profit. The modern method is mass production and distribution; low prices and moderate returns from enormous numbers. Given exceptional application, substantial capital and ample reserves with which to meet lessened demand and intense competition, it may prove successful. Some broiler producers have shown that it can be done. So have other technicians with other commodities.

The other, traditional, way, which given time and experience, is more in accord with the capital limitations of most people, is to produce high-quality poultry fully deserving of a higher price, appealing to the connoisseur and those who prefer their pullets to survive rather longer than the average. There is scope too for the breeder of the less popular breeds. Discriminating customers fancy something different and are prepared to pay higher prices. There was a time when show birds changed hands at fantastic prices. Even now American fanciers pay handsomely for exhibition fowls. An unusual variety is well worth breeding as a sideline. Even a bread-and-butter breed in the hands of an enthusiast can be made handsome as well as productive. There are cases on record of high profits from bantams and ornamental waterfowl.

Obvious examples are Rhode Island Reds of deep even colour, White Wyandottes guaranteed not to throw single combs, Light Sussex of old-fashioned type and size, and free from the tendency to revert to yellow legs. Other suggestions are North Holland Blues with better egg colour, and Marans capable of higher production without losing their exceptional egg colour. Faverolles, Malines, Croad Langshans, Orpingtons, Rocks, are very much better layers than is realized by those who regard them as purely ornamental. Once in a spirit of inquiry I crossed an Indian Game hen with a Scots Dumpy. The daughters averaged over 250 eggs apiece in their pullet year. Silkie X Wyandottes laid nearly as well. The scope is limitless for the creative enthusiast who is prepared to devote time and energy to what at worst is a fascinating project, at best a lucrative and satisfying business.

There is another aspect which deserves mention—these old breeds are not so prone to the modern scourges of fowl paralysis and lymphomatosis. Some strains are possibly very inbred and in consequence difficult to hatch and rear. To the breeder of resource this is a challenge.

The Leghorn enthusiasts may feel hurt at the exclusion of their favourites. The best of the Whites and Blacks are so good however that the less experienced are not likely to improve them. There are other varieties, Brown and Buff for instance, where competition is less intense. They all suffer from the real disadvantage of white eggs. Surplus cockerels are an embarrassment. Yet here too by selection they can be improved. I knew a strain of White Leghorns, now unfortunately dispersed, the males of which were full-breasted with short legs and wide flat backs.

Other, more or less non-sitting varieties, Bresse, Anconas, Houdans, Minorcas, are intrinsically valuable material for the stock improver who really likes poultry. Who will buy them in competition with bread-and-butter breeds and crosses? Who would have thought ten years ago that hybrids and miscegenates would ever achieve popularity? There are three reasons, clever advertising, determined salesmanship and merit. Yet their appeal is not universal, nor will it ever be. The fastidious require something better to look at. If they must keep poultry let them be handsome and different, and above all healthy.

For it has to be admitted that chickens are not what they used to be. It would be futile to assess the blame or list the possible causes. Those of us who have lived long enough to justify an opinion have no doubt that modern management and husbandry are more conducive to quantity than quality. That being so the greater the scope for the small man who is prepared to devote individual attention to his birds. The mass producer regards a flock as an entity, the stockman as a congregation of individuals.

Fortunately it is possible to produce the nucleus of a superb flock with very little capital. One can make a start long before becoming committed, gaining invaluable experience with one's own birds in a way that will not hurt much. One cannot learn poultry-keeping by books—not even from this. Some of us are distinctly sceptical of the written word. Many authors have never kept a bird of their own. Others have failed to make a success of them. It is easier to write and talk about them than to make them pay.

What follows is a true record of how the writer anticipated his retirement. If from now on he relapses into the first person singular it is in the interests of truth rather than self-advertisement.

Chapter 3

LEARNING THE HARD WAY

My professional experience goes back to the early 1920s. At that
time flocks were small and by modern standards remarkably
healthy. Deaths among pullets competing in Laying Tests were in
the region of 5 per cent. Ten years later they had reached over
20 per cent. My employers, an enlightened sub-committee of a
County Council, decided that there seemed no point in continu-
ing to trapnest potential corpses; the ratepayer's money could be
spent to better advantage. The details were left to me.

Not all flocks were disease ridden—there were exceptions.
Some of their owners and their methods I knew intimately. They
had two factors in common—small units and personal supervision.
They were without exception skilled and conscientious chick-
rearers. Some backyarders still used natural methods. On analysing
the casualty records at the County Laying Trial for which I was
responsible, theirs were significantly fewer than those of the
professional poultry-keepers.

So, when the Demonstration Smallholding came into being
the decision as to how to raise the breeding stock had already been
made. The technique and equipment had yet to be proved. Meanwhile every week chicks for sale for table purposes were being
hatched in second-hand incubators and reared in home-made
brooders. It was a salutary experience. It is not the easiest thing
in the world to design a brooding appliance that will rear good
chicks.

Grassland management, too, required investigation. It was
almost universally believed that poultry ruined pasture. In this
country at least there was no knowledge of the palatability of
the various species of grasses, clovers and herbs. Little was known
of the technique of resting. The textbooks recommended 200
birds to the acre irrespective of type of soil, climate, or breed.
Normally the layout of the enclosures comprised gangways, and

22

houses with alternate runs on either side—a most extravagant system requiring almost twice as much fencing as is necessary, and the laborious use of the scythe.

In a very short time all these problems were solved. An economical layout, with the almost complete absence of orthodox and expensive gates, was evolved. Hay-making, re-seeding, cropping on a miniature farm scale became easy. Walking was reduced to a minimum. Routine duties such as feeding, watering and egg collection could be carried out expeditiously. The old bugbear of waterlogged gangways no longer obtained. When the land reverted to a bona fide smallholding, the three acres of grass were in better condition than when acquired twelve years before.

To the modernist this concern for grass and its management may appear ill-timed and of no importance. Actually it has a very real bearing, not only on health, but on feeding costs, so much so that a very material saving can be made by those whose birds have access, ideally to good grass, or, failing grass, to vegetables. For grass contains, in addition to protein, valuable vitamins and minerals which are costly to buy.

My own interest in simple feeding dates back to the early 1930s. It seemed incomprehensible that the price of grain should be lower than that of middlings, that the part should be more expensive than the whole. Why should not the fowl do its own milling? Why such complex mixtures? The traditional food of fowls was whole grain, supplemented in spring and autumn especially, by grass, grubs, insects and maggots, protein, minerals and vitamins. Was the modern hen capable of subsisting and laying satisfactorily on a purchased ration of cereals and protein, plus what it could pick up from the earth?

Half a dozen Croad Langshan pullets with access to grass were given *ad lib* a mixture of cracked grain, split peas and granulated meat and bone. During the winter months production was excellent. With the warmer weather the birds lost condition and *scoured** badly. The diet was changed to wet mash and whole grain, whereupon the birds recovered and resumed the experimental feed. Again they reacted unfavourably. Once more they

*diarrhoea

23

were fed normally and recovered. By this time the *cracked* grain was definitely sour and musty. From then on it was fed whole. Despite the two checks, total production for the twelve months was over 1,200 eggs. In their second year on the same diet they laid and bred very successfully.

It was evident that the system of whole grain feeding was sound. Could the fowls satisfactorily balance their own requirements when grain and protein were offered separately? The answer had to await the end of the 1939–45 war when grain again became available. All my evidence shows that they can, that given adequate grass and/or greenfood and sunshine egg production is at least as profitable on this system as on orthodox mash or pellets.

As to the stock, it was at least as good as that with which the venture began. The housing, of original design, the fencing, the technique, had been proved. Subsequent experience has not disproved the belief that the laws of good poultry husbandry are few and simple; that to flout them will inevitably have painful repercussions.

The 'expert' had learned the hard way. How many newcomers will have had as much experience? They can, if they care to read, profit from mine.

At the age of forty-two I became a poultry-keeper in my own right, by purchasing half a dozen yearling hens. They were housed in a holding unit of my own design constructed for the most part from the remains of the garden fence. The covered end, 6 ft wide at base, 4 ft high at apex, contained perches over a retractable dropping-tray; below was a dust bath and, on either side nests and a food trough with access from outside.

In front was a wire-netting run, flat-topped, so that when, in the foreseeable future, the structure became too rickety for further towing, a roof could be superimposed and the fold converted into a static roost with scratching-shed. Meantime until food rationing was imposed in 1941 the standard diet was grain, peas, and granulated meat and bone, *ad lib*, plus of course oyster shell and flint grit. This contraption was moved over grass and crop residues alike.

24

to the greater fertility of the garden, and a considerable saving in the housekeeping account. As a matter of interest four of the hens—two were culled—laid 600 eggs between January and November.

Meanwhile replacement pullets had been hatched by one of the hens, in a combined coop and run, made from what was left of the fence boards. After the first week or two, when they were given oatmeal, minced house scraps and skim milk, the chicks subsisted on the same food as the hens. From ten days old they were given greenfood, lettuce, spinach, chopped onions; later cabbage, Scotch and perpetual kale. Their subsequent production, until the quality of the grain obtainable became too low even for my birds, was very satisfactory. When rationing became stringent and gain unprocurable they had to make do on meal with minced vegetables and house scraps. I had become a bona fide backyarder.

In five years I had five breeds, Malines, Sussex, Rhodes, Wyandottes and Croad Langshans, all acquired as hatching eggs from sources I knew well. Sometimes they hatched well, sometimes badly. Broody hens vary in steadfastness. The technique was unusual; it had to be. There was no time to take the hen off and replace her on the eggs. She had to make her own arrangements. Food and water were provided at the front end of the miniature fold; the nest—on the earth—was under cover but not separated from the run. This was boarded as to the sides and had a detachable lid, partly solid, the rest slatted. The virtue of this construction was that if she decided not to sit, her head was visible from afar. Moreover she had not broken her eggs.

There was a detachable end to the covered part with a gap at the apex through which she could be seen whilst sitting. One of the early lessons learnt was the necessity of masking it to exclude as far as possible any light, more especially for the first few days. Another was the desirability of ample litter, hay for preference. On one occasion I deliberately withheld it; the hen buried the eggs. On another I placed the eggs on level ground; they rolled all over the place. A shallow depression seems obligatory. Just how many eggs to set depends on their size and that of the hen. I have the impression that a hen prefers an even number. One of my best sitters will not tolerate thirteen—she either breaks or pushes aside the extra egg. It matters not what time of day or night she is introduced to the eggs. In most cases, however, it is better to set the hen in the late evening, quietly and gently. The site should be secluded and shaded, protected from wind, sun, and wandering animals.

It is not claimed that this technique is better than the textbook method. It is considerably simpler and less trouble. Without it breeding in my circumstances would have been impossible. With it and the right equipment breeding and rearing became possible, almost simple; even in my absence. I have set eggs before going on holiday and counted the chicks on my return. Sometimes they have been few, sometimes plenty. On occasions the eggs have been fouled or broken. The system is not perfect, but it works well with *good* broodies. Such are worth retaining to a ripe old age. It is seriously suggested that they should be line-bred for this very necessary function. Gamekeepers would appreciate them. So would breeders of non-broody varieties anxious to produce the very best stock.

As to vermin, the best and most convenient time to apply insecticide is before she is thoroughly broody, in the nest to which she is accustomed; failing that to her new nest. Beware of squirrels—they can ruin the results. I use traps and a catapult.
* For rats, Warfarin, if fresh, is infallible. My practice is to have a covered bait point alongside the coop. There remain grass-snakes and neighbours' cats. The answer to both is a good dog; the way to deter him from interfering with the chicks is to put him with the hen. That goes for your own cat too. Hell hath no fury like a broody hen with young.

When in my forty-seventh year I began seriously to prepare for my eventual retirement, I was glad to have a conscientious sitter. My decision as to choice of breed had been made. There was no need to look beyond the flock for which I had been responsible in my official capacity. Six hens and one cock, a half brother, were selected as my foundation stock. Among them was a hen of

*If rats have become 'Warfarin'-resistant, consult the local Council.

known quality, a very fast layer of a shapely brown, good-sized egg. Her physique left nothing to be desired—wide flat back, short widely spaced legs, tight feather, full breast, small pea comb, pure white plumage. She had—a weakness of mine—feathered shanks; just to be different.

So far as I could tell only her eggs were set. They hatched well. Her next mate was her son, her next her grandson by her son. So far the progeny had been excellent. By then it had become very uniform. All of both sexes had neat pea combs and small wattles. Why grow big ones? Most customers do not eat them.

The fourth mating was less successful; her great-grandson was the best specimen so far used. She herself in her fifth year was beginning to wilt. Her eggs had diminished in size. She went broody for the first time and raised a few chicks, then, her work completed, died.

I was left with a family of very inbred brothers and sisters. When in due course they were mated, each male in turn, the results were disastrous. Scores had died in the shell. For two seasons I persisted, and finally achieved three chicks. Of the three one was a cockerel, a tiny miniature. The two pullets never laid. So much for close inbreeding. Up to a point it had been very successful. Type had been fixed without detriment to physique or production in three generations. I had confirmed that the first warning is a high proportion of eggs that fail to hatch. Anyone contemplating a repetition of this experience is strongly advised to test the hen first for hatchability. There is no point in inbreeding to any bird not outstandingly good in all respects. Such are few. The success I achieved was due to the excellence of the bird, not to the system. And I still had her blood, very concentrated in the little cock.

I had also achieved a house of my own with an acre of land, half garden and orchard, the rest a more or less levelled brick-field. The garden was foul with most known weeds, the field a mass of nettles, horse-radish, mare's-tail, plantains, bindweed, agrostis. After rain it was waterlogged; a few wet days caused flooding. The land drains under the adjoining field emptied into my field. The overflow from my neighbour's pond had been piped by a previous owner who had run out of 6-in and finished off with 3-in drain pipes! The field was not fenced and all the dogs in the vicinity used it as a convenience.

The first priority, as always, was the stock. In addition to the little cock there were six white pullets and a hen, their mother, a distant relation acquired with a view to introducing fresh blood. There were also chicks sired by one of my two-year-old cocks lent to a breeder of Light Sussex, being brooded by a North Holland hen costing a pound.

One by one the white pullets prolapsed; so did their mother. Of the cross-bred Sussex, most died of various forms of paralysis or big liver. Meanwhile the little cock bred two black daughters out of the North Holland hen. The following year he was mated to one of these daughters and threw mainly white progeny. Eleven years later the black hen was still alive, the matriarch and founder of the revived strain.

Obviously outcrossing is not invariably unsuccessful. Equally the influence of the female is very potent. *Cherchez la femme.*

Chapter 4

FENCING AND CONTROLLED GRAZING

So much for the stock. The land, to my mind, was equally important. My half acre left much to be desired, in area and herbage. But it was all I had. The immediate necessity was to keep out intruders, dogs and foxes in particular. That meant fencing. I acquired every available roll of heavy gauge ex-landing-strip netting and as many metal stakes as I could transport.

Three sides of the nearly square field were wide open. The far boundary, at the original level, consists of a thick hedge with a narrow ledge above a steep drop. On the near side is the garden. A flight of steps leads down to a concrete air raid shelter—an obvious food store.

My first mistake was to erect the boundary fence at the end of the garden, that is, in view of the house. Feminine pressure and my own efforts put it out of sight. All I had to do was to cut the wire loops, uproot the uprights and re-erect the fence three yards from the foot of the bank, and erect a gate opposite the steps—incidentally the only gate. This arrangement is much more satisfactory. It allows room for a compost heap, a bonfire, the broody hen department, and unobstructed access to the blackberries on the bank, without interference from the geese—a matter of some concern to the womenfolk.

The other mistake was to assume that because the far hedge was thick it was necessarily foxproof. It was not, as one of the geese discovered to her cost and mine. There was a gap big enough for both fox and goose. So, precariously, I hacked back the hedge and erected more fencing alongside. Unfortunately for one of my Muscovy ducks I failed to peg it down securely. Another, or maybe the same, fox got his head through; his body followed. Incensed at this second loss I set a snare. Fortunately for my neighbour's cat I was up early next morning.

This experience taught me that if I was to sleep soundly I must look to my boundary. It indicated too that a fox is more likely to burrow than to climb, for my netting is only 5 ft high with a single strand of wire above, offset outwards. It is however very thick, 13 gauge in fact. No fox will bite through that; which is more than one can claim for ordinary 19 gauge chicken wire. The other vulnerable sides are now reinforced by a vigorous growth of quicks, brambles, *lonicera nitida* and privet. My fence increases in safety and stature every year. It will last my time.

Draining was obviously urgent. My intention was and is to keep fowls, not waterfowl. A few geese and Muscovy ducks to hatch the goose eggs, to help eat and improve the herbage for the time being; but only as a sideline. Here again in the light of experience my efforts might have been better directed. The ditch could just as easily have been made in straight lengths rather than in an arc.

It took up most of my spare time the whole of my first autumn and winter. Two spades were required, one to clear the other of blue clay and yellow clay. Midway a pond was excavated for the benefit of the web-footed. The gander was especially intrigued. He was my constant companion. From time to time he encouraged me by nibbling the seat of my trousers. When, eventually, the final grading had been completed and the water diverted to its new path, he was just as delighted as I. Incidentally the work qualified for a Government grant through the County Agricultural Executive Committee.

The effect was satisfactory so far as it went. Unfortunately it confirmed my suspicion that the middle of the field was the lowest point. Two more trenches were cut and filled in with, respectively, brushwood and brick ends. They both emptied into the pond. Another similar drain was cut below the nearer bank and joined to the main outlet. Only then did I lay down my third spade—two had disintegrated.

The following autumn it became necessary to clear the weeds from the sides and bottom of the ditch. In places it had been undermined by the hens and a rat. Removing the trash was an unpleasant and dirty job. A year later I straightened it, laid pipes and filled it in.

By that time I had subdivided the field into enclosures. Quite fortuitously the pond had been dug in the fence line so that two lots of fowls had access. Another water point was made just inside the third enclosure. The fourth was at the outlet where the water left my property. Here I inserted a metal grille to keep out marauders. Now during the autumn, winter and spring watering is automatic except for the nearest enclosure, normally reserved for the youngest and least thirsty chicks.

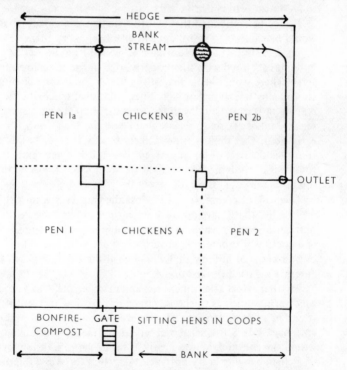

FIG. 4.   Layout for my ex-brickfield showing alternate enclosure and water points

These of course are inveterate escapists. If there is a gap they find it. The likelihood of their discovering the way back can be discounted. They fall ready victims to magpies and cats. Small-mesh netting 2 ft high is wired to the main fence. In the first instance it must be meticulously pegged; later the grass will grow through. Only then can the chicks be regarded as reasonably safe. Leave the gate open for a moment and they are through. Hunting for a black chick in a blackthorn hedge can be a painful and un-rewarding pursuit, locating it by voice is impossible. The only way to recover it is to enlist the aid of its mother; then pounce.

It may be contended that all this fencing costs money, that it would be cheaper to rear them and ultimately keep them intensively. In certain circumstances, second-hand houses or buildings acquired with the property, one might be inclined to agree. There would be no fear of the fox. If, however, the birds are to enjoy occasional or daily liberty in the absence of efficient fencing, it is somebody's job to fasten them up at night, *every night*. And of course to release them next morning, for it is in the early hours that the fox is most likely to call. Personally I do not begrudge the cost of fencing, steep though it is. I need not go the rounds if it is raining, and I can lie in late if I like; knowing that my birds can catch the early worm.

One can, of course, forget to close the gate. It is against this eventuality that I have devoted much time and brainpower to a number of devices which in theory should allow the ingress of hens and cocks whilst deterring unauthorised entry by fox or killer dogs. I know of nothing that will prevent the stoat or weasel from entering a slatted floored house.

My first effort after much trial and many errors, was a moderate success, inasmuch as the hens learned to negotiate it. I lent it to a friend in a fox-ridden area. He retrieved volpine hairs from the entrance. A Jack Russell terrier would not face it. Nor unhappily would the cockerel, he was nearly as big as the fox. I then reverted to a chain hanging in the entrance. Alas, that too was a failure. Whether the fox ignored it or enticed the occupants outside I shall never know. Dead hens don't talk. I then bethought me of

32

FIG. 5. Fox-deterrent gadget

Mr. Tom Turney of Northampton, who very kindly gave me one of his proved fox prodders, illustrated on this page. He assured me that, fitted to night arks on range, over a period of 15 years there had been only one fatality, but of course it is still necessary to let the birds out, earlier than appeals to me. For the early bird catcheth the worm, and the fox catcheth the early bird. For anyone contemplating a construction of such a device I must point out that the size and the length of the prodder are related to the dimensions of the exit and the variety of fowl. The measurements of the model portrayed are, height 12 in width 7 in stop 10 in. The hinges are mounted on the *inside*, thus allowing the fowl to pass under the nail or rod without damage, whereas the more the fox pushes the deeper it penetrates

It will by now have become evident that grass figures very prominently in my scheme of things. The classic method of improving herbage is by means of folding units. It is an effective technique, but there are several serious and expensive objections. The cost of housing is high, so is the depreciation. Folds have to be moved every day, wet or fine. For anyone with a slippery disc they are a hostage to fortune. With some makes of folds the birds can easily be hurt. Moreover the fresh grass does not normally last beyond breakfast time. The occupants have the rest of the day in which to savage each other. If the ground is wet the eggs are filthy; if dry the fowls do their best to construct a dustbath—only to have to start all over again next morning. Folding is in fact a very expensive way of muck-spreading.

Nevertheless the principle of rotational grazing is sound. Permanent enclosures with a constant number of occupants are bound to deteriorate. During the winter they are over-stocked and overgrazed, and rapidly become a mass of weeds. During the spring the birds cannot cope with the rapid growth, the grasses run to seed and depress the clovers. Folds become immobilized. In any case the menu is restricted. On real free range the birds have choice of herbs, legumes, grasses, maybe weeds, a little of what they fancy in fact. Moreover they can make a dustbath and eat earth—there are more things in Heaven and earth (and grass) than are dreamed of in the modern poultry-keeper's philosophy.

In my case it was necessary to persuade something other than weeds to grow. The only part of the field that produced any grass was in the corner near a square of concrete once the site of a pigsty. It was mainly perennial rye grass, with here and there a clump of cocksfoot, and a lot of tall fescue.

Ploughing and reseeding was out of the question. It was impossible to introduce a four-wheeled tractor. My good neighbour could not be persuaded to lend me his two-wheeled rotary—the reason was obvious when I began digging the ditch. Brickbats and burnt clay are not good for rotor blades. Any improvement therefore would have to be effected by the fowls. Or geese. Hence the first drinking point.

I obtained a trio of White Chinese. Not that they are, in my experience, the most assiduous of grazers or sitters. But they are good layers and most attractive to look at. One can be forgiven for wishing their voices were more melodious. Their base was the pond, their function grass improvement. They were penned by 2 ft netting in a narrow enclosure which was gradually extended. The fence was held upright by metal rods through the mesh. After wrestling with 50 yd of netting and numerous stakes, it occurred to me that it would be easier to move every other stake, forming a zigzag, alternately.

There was initially very little nourishment. They subsisted largely on stale bread. In the intervals between meals they padded up and down just inside the fence, grumbling. Their enclosure became a mixture of mud and manure; an ideal medium for grass seeds. Many of them took. The linnets, tits and sparrows were driven off by the geese. In the process their great feet rolled in the seedlings.

I sowed Italian rye grass, palatable, winter-green, and at that time cheap. It was distributed by finger and thumb at the rate of 20 lb per acre, i.e. 1 oz per 15 sq yd. The geese co-operated admirably. So too will ducks, other than Muscovies—they fly over the fence. Hens are no help—they eat the seeds.

In due course my barren, sour, and unproductive wilderness became relatively fertile. By now I had acquired some Muscovies, primarily to hatch the goose eggs. They made excellent sitters and foster mothers, and better grazers than other varieties of ducks. Meantime the fowls were increasing in number. The grass and weeds responded to the generous manuring and became something of an embarrassment. A friend gave me an ancient scythe. The blade was worn but had the authentic ring. I learnt the hard way how to set and whet it—a dying art. The safest method is to hold the blade vertically, point down, on the grass, edge inwards, and stroke it, not more than twenty times, on either side alternately, from heel to point. With a keen blade and dew on the grass, late evening or early morning, I know of no more satisfying sound nor more pleasing method of retaining one's figure. And nothing more frustrating than hitting a stone and losing, always irretrievably, a wedge. Then another friend gave me a snead with a ball joint head. More recently I bought cheaply a rotoscythe. After trying vainly to retain the grass-box in position with the cutter set low, I procured a metal plate which directs the cut grass and the fumes downwards. With this machine I kept the grass in the chick enclosure really short. But I prefer the swish of my scythe to the staccato of the machine. My grass had justified my efforts. It remained necessary to ensure that it continued to improve. It is a very simple matter to allow the hens to ruin it.

The rules of grassland management are nearly as simple. The most important is to stock heavily during the growing season and lightly during the winter; and so far as is practicable to avoid grazing an enclosure during the late winter two years in succession. For it is then that the best and earliest and most palatable species are beginning to grow. Naturally the birds will consume them, to the greater benefit of the less palatable varieties and the weeds. After a few years of this treatment the weeds, plantains, may-weed and groundsel particularly, will have taken charge. The only solution will be reseeding. And if overgrazing in winter continues then reseeding will again be necessary. This time a bare fallow will be required—a costly business that can be avoided, if the rules are followed.

Fortunately in most flocks the numbers are at a minimum during the winter. Moreover the older birds, moulting or not yet back in lay, are not nearly so active as the pullets. These should be on grass that has had a long rest, never on young seeds—they will tear the heart out of them. Old hens, young chicks, cockerels, perhaps; but never laying pullets, until the sward is really established.

Spring grass requires entirely different treatment. It must be heavily stocked, at the rate of several hundred birds per acre. If this is not practicable by letting out birds that have been kept intensively, or acquiring calves or lambs, it must be laid up for hay and the birds moved to a smaller enclosure.

It is not generally known that one can influence the composition of the sward, more particularly the ratio of clover to grass, by management. If the clover predominates, let the grass grow and take a hay crop. If on the other hand clovers are thin, graze hard.

As to fertilizers, they may or may not be necessary on some land. On my brick-field in nine years nothing, not even lime or chalk, has been applied. Nor has it been harrowed except by the birds, which have been encouraged, by broadcasting grain among bent and weeds, ground elder in particular, to scratch for their living.

In a garden ground elder can be a menace. On the headland it is a simple matter to poison it—and everything else—with weed-killer; if you like that sort of thing. Among soft fruit, currants and gooseberries, there are two alternatives: removal of the bushes, which is recommended; and infinite patience, defoliation of the weed every time it throws a fresh leaf. Even bell-bine, convolvulus, bind-weed or whichever pet name you have for it, cannot withstand that sort of treatment indefinitely. It took me seven years! And, of course, the constant hoeing and forking did not do the bush roots any good.

My greatest triumph however was the eradication of ground elder from a well-established and prolific rhubarb bed. That took less than a year.

In the autumn I acquired scores of paper meal sacks and laid them down methodically over the whole area. During the night the wind blew them all ways. Next time I covered them with heavy netting and spare fence posts. Heavy rain completed the seal. By early spring the sacks were sufficiently softened as to allow the rhubarb to force its way through.

Then followed the tedious part of the treatment. With a fork I removed all the rhizomes I could—and some of the rhubarb—without doing too much damage, throwing the roots on top of

37

the sacks previously dumped on the headland. The hot sun did
the rest.

A week or two later I repeated the performance, forking,
pulling and patiently working out the diminishing weakened
roots with my fingers. By mid-summer I had a bonfire of
rhizomes and sacks. And, between ourselves, I was rather pleased
with myself.

Nettles are another nuisance, but more palatable. Cut, and
allowed to wilt, hens will eat them eagerly. Cut and fed straight
away turkeys love them. True they pick up their feet gingerly
after walking over them but given the opportunity and no other
form of greenfood they will cheerfully graze them.

Sodium chlorate will kill nettles. It should be applied before
they have made much growth—that way it gets to the roots.
But have a care. Do not get the solution on your trousers; or
spill any on the floor then drop a lighted match, as I did
absent-mindedly on one hectic occasion.

My system of folding is based on the technique employed by
shepherds for arable sheep. Instead of wattle hurdles the
material is heavy netting of uniform length. A very convenient
size is 12½ yd long, i.e. half a 25-yd roll; dimensions of wire 3-in
mesh, 13 gauge, stiffened at either end by ½-in round rods. This
very durable fencing is no longer available. On my next holding I
shall use chain link fencing of similar dimensions.

The corner posts are made of 1-in tube 6 ft long. Twelve
inches from the base is welded a 2-ft right-angled prong which
when driven into the ground keeps the main tube vertical. The
ends of the tube are squashed for ease of entry. On heavy land
it is as well to ease the task of driving by making holes with a
crowbar. Removing the post is even simpler. The crowbar is
inserted under the horizontal part of the forked upright; a little
upward pressure and out it comes.

An alternative to tubes is angle iron; more is required viz.
18 ft instead of 8 ft. They should however last longer, for sooner
or later water will get into the tubes and cause rust in the base.
With angle iron the 6 ft upright is sunk 1 ft in the ground, the

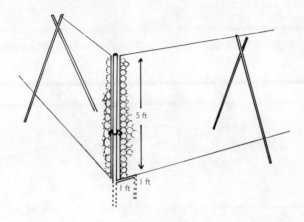

two struts also 6 ft are bolted to the uprights near the top. The base of each strut is drilled to accommodate a metal peg. See illustration p. 40.

These corner posts are erected 12½ yd apart. The netting is held in position by 6 gauge galvanised wire coiled centrally round the upright, bent at either end into a hook. Two types are used, one bent at right-angles to secure the transverse fences, the other straight to hold the adjoining length of netting.

How to hold the fence upright between the corner posts taxed my ingenuity for quite some time. The obvious way was to sink more vertical posts and secure the netting by loops. That would have defeated the whole object of the exercise, rapid erection and dismantling. The solution is delightfully simple—bipods, two 6-ft lengths astride the fence, the selvedge gripped in the angle produced by pinning the two component parts 3 in from the top. These have proved most effective and neater than one would think. They are adjustable for height and can cope with any unevenness in the ground. There is no need for pegs—the weight of the netting is sufficient to deter the occupants from crawling beneath. The bipods can be constructed of metal, or more cheaply of 1-in square battens, secured by 2-in nails

39

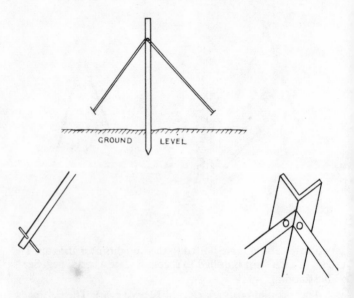

FIG. 7. Corner post assembly—angle iron

driven through each and punched at the head, allowing the point to be clinched on the other side.

So much for the material, strong, flexible and adaptable. With it one can make an enclosure of any size, any shape, square, rectangular, triangular, even circular, with access to the interior never more than 6 yd away. Single-handed it is a perfectly simple job to dismantle and erect whenever and wherever one desires.

For moving a flock single-handed a spare length and three bipods can be rapidly erected to prevent a break-away; two lengths can make a corridor. With an assistant at the other end of the netting the birds can be shepherded in the right direction.

For a static layout, in practice the first enclosure is usually set up at the nearest corner, in conjunction with the boundary

FIG. 7a. Bipods similar to fence supports, equally useful for beans

fence, requiring two lengths of wire only. From this beginning
one can extend forward or sideways. In my case I decided on
utilizing the sides for the adults, leaving the immediate fore-
ground for the young chicks and the rectangle beyond for the
growers. Each adult pen has an alternative enclosure. The houses
are sited centrally giving access at will to either, depending of
course on the state of the herbage. During the winter, if need be,
the hens can be allowed on the young birds' enclosures, normally
vacated by the autumn. Thanks to this routine, judicious broadcasting of the scratch feed and the assistance of the geese, plus
reseeding—about which more anon—my ex-brick-field now grows
grass, palatable food-saving grass, which each year becomes denser
and more nutritious. Clover now runs where there used to be
black grass and bents. These are being steadily reduced by the
birds.

The reeds, thanks to draining, have disappeared. The wild

vetches are being reduced. Horse-radish regrettably persists. Docks and ragwort are pulled out by hand. I hesitate to enlist the aid of sprays and hormones. I would use pigs—if I had more land. They would deal with the docks. Would they cope with horse-radish?

This method of controlled grazing has been adapted to my particular circumstances, a small field almost square, small units in small houses capable of being moved if necessary but normally static for convenience. The birds have been rotated round the houses. The houses and netting could, just as simply but more arduously, have been moved round the field. Had the area of land been greater, say an acre, and the number of birds in the region of a hundred, the requirements in terms of netting would have been four rolls. These would enclose an area 25 yd square, approximately an eighth of an acre. When the birds began to fly over, the unit would be moved on. They would be retained in the house while the two sides of the enclosure A and C were moved forward, joined by the leading section B. A feed of grain in the fresh grass would encourage them in the right direction, after which the house and the remaining side would follow. The whole operation might take a quarter of an hour.

There are alternatives to my fencing, but so far as I know nothing so effective at the price. One clever device is an electric hurdle, the frame and base of cedar wood, the rest of wire netting and wire. It is claimed to be foxproof. Certainly the hens give it a wide berth. Unfortunately it is so costly that to enclose a large area would be prohibitive. A small area would have to be moved frequently if the birds were to obtain much nourishment from the grass.

Attempts have been made to utilize electric fencing, two strands or more. The most successful I know necessitated a certain amount of training of the hens. Grain was scattered under the wire. The knowledgeable hens kept their distance, the more trusting took the bait. After a peck or two they lifted their heads. The effect was shattering—they literally jumped to it. A more recent innovation is nylon netting. In the right circumstances—that is in the absence of pigs, badgers, and rabbits—it is

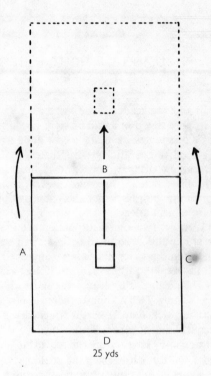

FIG. 8. Mobile house and enclosure for 100 fowls

effective; a girl can easily move it. I have no first-hand knowledge of fishing-nets, preferably recently tarred—they would seem to have possibilities as internal partitions. Like nylon they can be used for the upper portion of the fence, the lower consisting of heavy gauge netting or chain link. The more floppily it is erected the more difficult it is for the fox to climb.

43

Chapter 5

HOUSING WITHOUT HIRE
PURCHASE

My housing is all home-made; the newest is an ark with
retractable manure-tray over a ground floor giving shelter for
dusting, and access to nests and, if need be, food-troughs and
water. It is a good house, efficiently ventilated, mobile on skids,
capable of accommodating two dozen fowls upstairs. They can
be caught through a hatch in one side—always providing that they
do not sleep on the floor, as sometimes happens when pullets are
transferred from night arks.

Of these there are two, one incorporated in a folding unit
now no longer movable. What used to be the run is now covered
by corrugated iron sheets forming a scratching-shed. At the rear
is the ark. It has a split roof through which the birds can readily
be handled. The manure falls through the slats, which can be
removed for cleaning. This is an infrequent occurrence as the
whole structure is jacked up. A nest is attached at one end.

The other ark is identical in all functional respects with its
prototype made in 1936 at the special request of a little lady
who wanted a poultry house which she could use for brooding,
rearing and laying. It was quite a commission and took quite a
while to design.

It had to be simple for I am not a trained craftsman; no half-
joints, no mortices, no clever carpentry; just nails, preferably
galvanized, screws and bolts. The critics all agreed that it was
fundamentally unsound as it had no frame as such. The cladding
was $\frac{3}{8}$-in tongued and grooved prime cedar, nailed horizontally
to vertical battens 2 in × 1 in at either end. The corner assembly
was bolted.

In my first models I used for the floors heavy gauge wire
netting with 2 in × 1 in battens laid across on top. They were

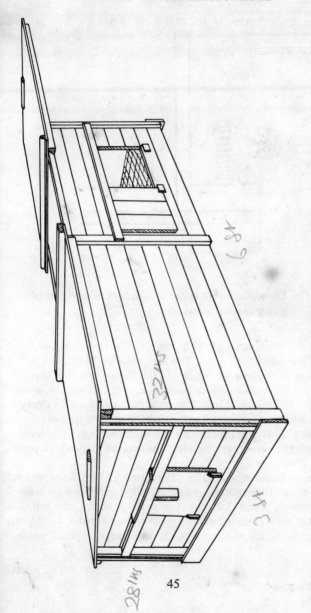

FIG. 9. Night ark, showing split, sliding roof, all-round ventilation and horizontal sliding exit covers

45

PLAN OF CORNER ASSEMBLY

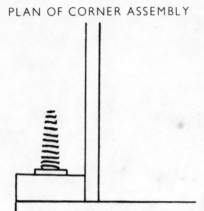

FIG. 10. Corner assembly detail of night ark draught proofing,
giving clean interior

lighter and more easily cleaned than slats. Nowadays Weldmesh
would seem desirable, 3 in × 1 in for chickens, 2 in × 2 in for
adults, so as to allow the manure to fall through more easily. The
floor is supported on rods or tubes $\frac{3}{8}$ in or ½ in diameter, located
accurately below the 2 in × 1 in cedar battens. It can be cleaned
with a wire brush. It may be held that the battens are not
necessary. True, but I think they are worth while as though only
1 in high they encourage the chickens from an early age to perch
rather than crowd.

The roof boards, also tongued and grooved, run the same way
as the slope. They must be cramped really tight. A recent brain-
wave is to use 3 in × 2 in, cut at an angle of 30 deg, one half to
carry the roof, the corresponding half the roof frame. The former
is mounted on the verticals with the wider edge upwards, giving

46

the same effect as angle iron, preventing any movement, in or out, of the top of the ark. The other half is attached to the roof boards, wider edge down. This arrangement effectively prevents movement upwards. In earlier models using 2 in × 1 in for both purposes and iron brackets, it was not unusual in a really high wind to have the roof blow away.

There is no need for felt. It is in fact undesirable and a constant temptation to the geese and calves. I do not recommend creosote; bitumen paint if you like, though I very much doubt if it is necessary. Actually untreated cedar looks most attractive. These little structures made very largely with my own fair hands are still in use twenty-five years later.

The inside dimensions I knew, 6 ft long, 3 ft wide, the extent to which average arms can reach. The height at the back should, for my small lady, not exceed 28 in. The front should be at least 4 in higher so as to throw off the rain; a lean-to requires less material and less skill than the pent-roof type.

Since then I have made arks to this specification from soft wood, hardboard, ply and cedar, still in my opinion the best from all points of view except cost. It is light, vermin-proof and neither shrinks nor swells.

Its original features—they have been widely copied—are: outside framework, giving a completely clean interior; 1 in all-round ventilation at the eaves and both ends; transverse skids facilitating single-handed movement; air inlet 6 in below the roost and really draughtproof; horizontal exit shutters. The roof is in two halves sliding on runners which also serve as baffles for the top ventilation. It is this split roof in particular that makes the ark so universally useful. Handling the birds is quick and comfortable for handler and handled alike. There is no excuse for failure to cull. Normally my fowls go to bed and get up when they like. When handling becomes desirable they are fastened in overnight and caught next morning. There is no fuss, no escaping and the minimum of excitement.

The roof is, of course, wholly removable. Thus one can change the furniture at will, wire floor, solid floor, brooder, hay-box canopy, hopper or trapnest. These two latter can be inserted,

FIG. 11. Nest detached from ark

FIG. 12. Nest, showing retractable egg drawer

48

the hopper inside the front door, the nest, inside or attached outside, at the other end. That is the reason for the extra pop-hole. In my case, not being in a position to trapnest, an outside nest is used. It has two floors, one level, of 16 gauge, 2-in mesh netting, through which the egg falls to a close mesh netting tray sloping rearwards retractable like a drawer. In size the nest is 3 ft, i.e. the width of the ark, by 2 ft, sufficient for twenty-five birds; for not all of them lay at the same time. One has to admit that wire floors are not comfortable and do not encourage the occupants to linger. Nevertheless if the grass in the enclosure is kept short and the birds have never known anything more luxurious they will use it. It is advisable however to bait it with hay or straw in the first instance. In wet weather it is a boon, and at all times a deterrent to egg-eating: moreover if an egg is cracked the contents fall through to the ground below.

Points to note are, it must fit snugly to the end of the ark, otherwise draughts can occasion discomfort, crowding and possibly colds; the laying floor must be *below* the level of the slatted or weld-mesh roost, otherwise some dirty beasts will surely sleep, and worse, in the nest.

When trapnesting is resumed plywood or hardboard 12 in wide will be placed across the floor of the ark, and a detachable front, two partitions, and three trapnests, sufficient for a breeding pen of twelve, installed. To release the occupants one pushes forward the roof, coupled to its other half, removes the egg, drops the hen on the floor, and pulls back the roof.

Cleaning out could not be simpler. Overturn the ark, sweep up the manure and cart it away; or if preferred fit a dropping-board resting on the ground, or, rather more complicated, fit legs and runners. Even the best of houses have their weaknesses. This has two, both fortunately easy to circumvent. Because the exit is at floor level it is desirable to close it at night, unless the site is exceptionally sheltered. If the flock consists of fifty birds the obvious thing to do is to have two arks facing each other. That way the other failing, a tendency in a really exposed position to blow over, is prevented.

49

FIG. 13.   Windbreak and dustbath

In my circumstances, the birds have the use of covered scratching-sheds, derelict folding units; a boon in really bad weather. If these were not available it would be necessary to provide simple open-fronted lean-to shelters with side entrances and a steep roof; they could serve various purposes, as a temporary nest or a shelter for young chicks if the ark is being used as a brooder; as it very well can be.

The choice of brooding equipment is wide, hovers, infra-red lamps, Putnams, warm floors. For cold brooding purposes a square frame carrying a blanket, sagging in the middle can be hung from the sides and end. In short this adaptable little structure can perform all the functions of specialized equipment at considerably less cost. In the south of England at any rate there is no need for any other, unless one is using natural methods of hatching and rearing.

For the more conventional technique it can be fitted to a folding chassis in a moment, without nuts and bolts. To this can be attached a cranked-axle wheeled device which lifts the rear end of the fold clear of the ground. One walks backwards a few yards, lets go, and the fold sits down again. On a reasonably level surface it is not easy for the chicks to escape nor for the fox, without digging, to nose his way beneath. It is complete protection against coccidiosis, crows and magpies.

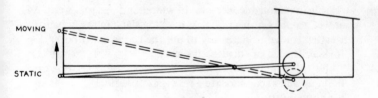

MOVING

STATIC

FIG. 14. Retractable wheel assembly for fold brooder

My other original piece of outdoor furniture is a miniature fold, 5 ft long, 2 ft wide. It is built around two isosceles triangles of 2 in × 1 in, with the base screwed or nailed to the sides, *not* half jointed. At the front is a truncated triangle, the sides 16 in high. Four boards each 5 ft long are nailed to the outside of the three frames. The rear end is completed by two 2 ft boards, and a metal ridge cap. The front is boarded. The back is another isosceles triangle with the framework, on the inside, produced downwards for ½ in or so, in such a fashion that it can be located inside the base of the triangular frame. It is held at the top by a button or a peg. This is the exit and entrance for hen and chicks.

The top of the run consists of a narrow rectangular frame boarded at the rear, slatted in front. It can be detached whilst the grain and water are replenished. The containers, in my case tobacco or coffee tins, are placed in the angles where they cannot so easily be fouled or knocked over. The triangular shape needs less room than the rectangular when stored and gives some measure of protection to the chicks. The hen, by reason of her size, is bound to remain central, whereas the baby chicks can avoid being kicked around. If they cannot, they are better dead.

Recently I have constructed a rather smaller version 4 ft X 1 ft 8 in from exterior hardboard, gradually replacing the old wooden ones. The hens have registered no objection.

These combined coops are all that is needed for hatching and rearing in reasonable weather. In winter and persistent rain it is as well to place a sheet of glass over the slats. In really bad weather it may be necessary to put the coops under cover, a makeshift shed of corrugated sheets.

No other housing is required. With arks and coops one can build up and accommodate a really sizeable flock of superbly healthy poultry.

It was obvious however that my technique though good enough for a hobbyist could not be recommended for the more ambitious, aiming at a flocksize of hundreds rather than dozens. Surely the job could be rationalised and speeded up?

For winter and bad weather hatching some form of overhead cover is essential. I have on occasion utilized corrugated sheets alongside each wall of a shed, accommodating four broody hens. Arctic conditions are not conducive to good hatching. A good hen deserves more comfort.

My first effort was a simple shallow box 6 ft X 12 in X 12 in with five partitions accommodating six broodies. It had a solid top and a hinged lid over the nest. It was deliberately dark, in

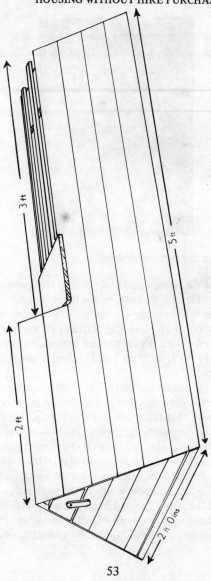

FIG. 15. Dual purpose coop and run

FIG. 16. Coop for hen and chicks

the interests of the hens. Food and water in troughs were
available at the far end. The rats found them first. One of them,
a female, decided to emulate the broodies. The hatch was to say
the least disappointing; worse, the pregnant rat escaped. At the
time I wondered if a cat would prevent a recurrence. Instead I
thought back to the time when I had utilised trap-nests—with
moderate success.

They were parked on the earth floor, which necessitated much
bending (a) to lift the trap front and allow the inmates off the
nest (b) to ensure that there was no doubling up. When there was,
in the progress of segregation eggs became broken and tempers
frayed. I had however thwarted the rats by introducing one of my
self-closing grain hoppers. I was not satisfied. One reason I have
mentioned, potential backache; another, too much fraternising,
probably due to the excessive width of the entrance; a third, the
dimensions of the nest 12 in × 12 in × 12 in, insufficient for a
big hen; and fourthly I frequently managed to scalp myself on
entering and leaving the broody shed. Why enter anyway, save in
an emergency?

My ideas began to crystallise. Why not an apex type house with windows at eye level on either side, so that the attendant can see at a glance all the nests and all the truants, of which there should not be many. If, as I stipulate, all the eggs are of the same age it is immaterial if the hens do not return to their original quarters. In any case they go on hunger strike for the first few days, sometimes as long as a week. They soon learn the way back; they have a strong homing instinct. Can it be by smell?

How to release them without entering the shed required thought and experiment. My first effort was only a partial success. I mounted a 6 ft length of 1 in × 1 in in bearings at each end with a handle just inside the door (I dared not produce it through the end wall as it would have presented too much of a temptation to my young inquisitive neighbours). To the 1 in × 1 in I fixed five nest fronts which when hanging more or less vertically kept the hens inside their 14 in nest—more or less. For a really vigorous hen could push it open, and did.

My latest (and final?) amendment was to substitute for the hinged version a sliding front. The top and bottom runners are joined by vertical boards 7 in wide which effectively seal the nests when lined up opposite the entrance. It will of course be understood that these also are 7 in wide, just about wide enough for a biggish hen.

In a small-boy proof locality I would of course produce the framework of the slide through the end wall. It would be as well also to provide a peephole or window to avoid accidental decapitation. The dimensions of the shed and the length of the nestboxes would depend upon the size of the flock; 12 ft × 6 ft should be ample for 20 hens, ten each side. A sliding front much longer might prove to be cumbersome and too heavy to move smoothly. In any case the workmanship should be of a reasonably high standard: an occasional dressing of soap or grease is recommended.

The water trough can be replenished from outside, the grain hopper located just inside the door, which should be locked. It does not require too much ingenuity to fasten the sliding front— either open or shut.

It may be asked where are the early broodies to come from? The answer is from early-hatched pullets, artificially lighted. Not that early hatching is essential on a breeding establishment and there is much to be said in favour of waiting for better weather. It is true that late-hatched pullets do not lay until Christmas. But their mothers do—large eggs at a time when they are at a premium. There is no necessity for incubators. Even so I would not rule them out completely; but never for future breeding stock.

I have known several instances of large-scale natural hatching; one where a thousand broodies were set every year. An old cow-shed was divided into sections with tiers of sitting-boxes along the walls. All the hens in each section were set on the same day. After being released to feed, drink and dust-bath, they were allowed to return on their own. If they went to another hen's nest it mattered not. The attendant let off each section in turn, lifting the weighted sacking from the fronts of half a dozen nests at a time. He then went the rounds again and dropped the sacking.

The same method on a smaller scale was employed by a breeder in Sussex until quite recently. In 1947, the coldest spring within most people's memory, his results were:

Hens set	Eggs set	Eggs broken	Clears	Addled	Dead in Shell	Chicks
156	2048	36	309	18	80	1605

During the same period I failed to find any comparable results from incubators, ancient or modern.

Chapter 6

HANDLING AND SELECTION

To watch a novice trying to catch a fowl and, if successful, to hold it, makes strong men weep. A bird on the ground is not too easy to apprehend, even if one succeeds in cornering it. If on a perch, grab its legs; at floor level its wings, not its tail, unless you are in need of pipe cleaners; nor its neck—unless it is a goose or duck—for it can scratch painfully.

One of the real problems of large flocks is how to catch the individual. In my experience a crook is useless. If I do manage to hook a leg it belongs to the wrong bird. I use an oversized butterfly-net made of a broomstick, hoop iron and pig netting. But not in a deep-litter house; for obvious reasons. Outside in an enclosure I persuade my quarry along the side netting as though to head her off. When she doubles back she runs straight into the net. I do not recommend chasing her and bringing the net down on her back—it is a simple matter to crack her skull. It is better for all concerned to take thought for the morrow, close the pop-hole at night and catch the occupants via the split roof next morning.

For the less active there is an alternative, a catching-crate, with a drop shutter at one end and a hinged or sliding hatch on top through which the birds can be extracted. The entrance should be the same size and at the same height as the pop-hole against which it is placed. The fowls are then encouraged to vacate the house, ark or shelter. The last lot are sometimes reluctant—which is another reason why I advocate my size of ark.

If the birds are to be removed any distance, a sledge is a worthwhile adjunct; or the crate can be fitted with skids or wheels. I have made an all-purpose trolley with a board floor, the sides and one end of wire netting; the other consists of a drop-door running in vertical grooves. Mounted on a pair of wheels salvaged from an old water-carrier, it is normally used for transporting weeds, leaves and other compost material, logs, litter, hay; anything bulky in

FIG. 17. Home made trolley transports leaves, garden rubbish and poultry: sliding hatch at one end

fact. Screwed into the top frame are hooks. To convert the vehicle into a catch-and-carry crate one needs only a sack on top.

With my type of housing handling is simple—as it ought to be— otherwise it is postponed, at the risk of losing by death a potential meal. It follows that handling should be regular. A good poultry-man does not allow his birds to die. Nor does he kill a bird just because it was hatched the previous year. To him pullets, hens, and cocks are individuals. If he breeds, as I do, he notes at an early age the outstanding youngster, the wide shoulders and stance, the early neat feathering, the sturdy limbs, the high wing carriage. Such a promising chick, if wing-banded, is noted in the record book and/or marked with a special leg band. And should it fail to live up to its early promise it is discarded. Hard but essential.

The qualities in an adult bird that appeal to me will bear

58

FIG. 18. Trolley—catching crate

FIG. 19. Proud of them

enumerating. They relate almost exclusively to physique and physical condition. The bird should be held head towards the handler, with its breastbone resting on the palm of one hand, in my case the right, with thumb and first finger gripping one thigh, the remaining fingers round the other. It takes almost no time to inspect both eyes, for roundness of pupil and clearness of iris, a very real indication of health. With the other hand I gauge the width across the hips and rub the feathers the wrong way. If they spring back of their own accord, if they are short and wide, I am satisfied. If, on the other hand, they are loose, long and narrow I am dubious. If the feathering on the thighs and flanks is copious and baggy the bird does not please me—I have a theory that such a bird is a slow moulter, and in its second year a slow layer.

By now with my right hand I have felt for the pelvic bones. In a good bird whether she is in lay or not, they are not covered with fat or gristle. The quality of the abdominal skin is of importance. If one can feel one's own fingers through it, well and good. If it is lined with fat, not so good; through here it must be stressed that with age comes a tendency to put on fat. A good hen will soon lay it off. It is inexcusable in a pullet. A very heavy bird, irrespective of age, should be ruthlessly eliminated. So much for the qualities that characterize a good layer.

In a general-purpose breed such as mine table properties are equally important. The most important is a relative shortness of leg. This is normally accompanied by width between the thighs. Such a bird has usually a wide well-fleshed breast. If the breastbone at the fore end bends into the wishbone without a pronounced angle, all the better. Such a conformation, in male birds particularly, is by no means common. No good table fowl when viewed from the side on a dish has a high angular profile. Compare for instance a Leghorn male with a pheasant.

So much for the really good bird, easily recognized on the ground, a good mover, active and alert. There is by contrast no difficulty in picking out the bad bird, sluggish, loose-feathered, narrow, shallow; to anyone with eyes to see unthrifty, if not actually ill or diseased. No observant poultryman would allow

FIG. 20. Seven years old

such a bird house-room. There is no need for handling. Her
appearance condemns her; there is no excuse for allowing her to
have fallen into such a state. Similarly the grossly overfat bird with
the massive protruding, sometimes 'sunburnt', abdomen should
receive short shrift. A rough-and-ready guide to culling for the
novice is the weight of the bird in hand. If she is nothing but skin
and bone, kill her. If she feels like a lump of lead, salvage her for
the table before she cheats you by dying. Such a hen, if held with
head slightly downward—not upside down, which can be fatal—
will probably assume a purple tinge about the face, appear
distressed and short of breath.

If hens were all obviously good or bad the inexperienced
would not suffer so keenly in trying to arrive at a decision. One
can sympathize; it is too bad to discard a good one. It is worse
to retain a dud. And it must be admitted that culling is not an

61

FIG. 21. Bold front; protein container in background constructed from two oil drums

exact science. Even the most skilled can make mistakes. A bird can exhibit all the textbook qualifications of a heavy layer—and never lay an egg. She can visit the nest regularly and cackle loudly,

62

FIG. 22. Dominant white cock

to no purpose. Her pelvic bones can be far apart and the point of the breast-bone many fingers breadth away, yet she does not lay. The really knowledgeable handler will probably identify her as a yolk-absorber. There is a feeling of overfullness about her abdomen that excites his suspicion. He may ring her as a dubious character. In my case she goes into a coop. If there are no eggs within a few days, she goes the way of all flesh.

Again, a bird may be still in moult when her mates are returning to lay. What to do, wait or kill? If the decision is to wait, where? Not in the flock, preferably, but in a coop or cage, or a small pen where she can be watched. If she begins to eat avidly, give her three weeks at most. I have no love of battery cages, but as a certain means of checking one's judgment or learning one's craft there is much to be said in their favour. For I know of no short cut to this aspect of a poultryman's knowhow. He must learn to cut his losses, not only to save on feeding costs but for the sake of the rest of the flock. One hen's biggest enemy is another, sick, hen especially under modern overcrowded conditions.

She should be liquidated. You may be lucky enough to persuade a local butcher or dealer to collect and, perhaps, to pay a reasonable price. But it is unlikely that he will show any interest in one or two. That means that you will have to learn the technique of killing and plucking, at least; if the most is to be made of the carcase it will have to be eviscerated also. A trio of jobs that I detest.

Killing is normally by dislocating the neck. The bird should be held by the legs in the left hand, breast downwards at waist level. The right hand should grasp the head of the bird between first and second fingers, the thumb under the throat. Stretch the neck downwards, at the same time bending the hand inwards; that is towards the wrist. The spinal cord is broken. Death is quick and clean—unless by your failing to arch the wrist, the unfortunate fowl loses its head. For that reason and in the interests of humanity it is well to practise on a dead bird. If the technique cannot be mastered, and if larger poultry, geese, turkeys or ducks, are kept, a proprietary poultry humane killer should be acquired. The neck of the victim is inserted and the lever brought over smartly. An adjustable stop prevents decapitation.

There are other methods, by knife, axe or gun, but they are messy and make plucking unpleasant. As for de-gutting it is revolting but inevitable.

How to tell the sex of chickens. And by that I do not mean hiring a sexer, for personally I deplore the technique. It is of course an advantage to the hatchery man with specific orders for pullets. One cannot help sympathizing with the hundreds of millions of cockerels whose short life is brought to an abrupt end by drowning or gassing.

Really skilled sexers are quick and gentle, others not so. Some

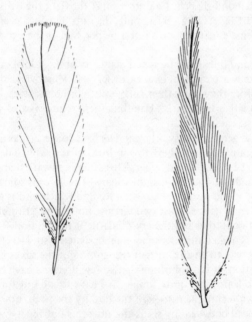

FIG. 23. Chicken feathers from small of back: on left female, on right male, 10 weeks of age

breeders will not subject their chicks to such indignity. Rightly or wrongly they believe it may result in permanent damage. One I know is convinced that manually sexed pullets are more prone than those not manipulated to prolapse, mis-shapen eggs, and ovarian disorders.

In my case I have a pretty shrewd idea how many of each sex there are by the time the chicks are three weeks old. The 'boys' have bolder heads, longer necks, a hint of red about the face, sparser feathering on back and wings and no semblance of a tail. The 'girls' have finer features, neater feathering, and distinct tails.

At ten weeks one can be positive. By that time the feathers on the back are patently different, those of the male definitely pointed almost diamond-shaped. Held up against the light the denser central part tapers to a sharp point, the outside fringe even more so. The female feathers are shorter, wider, and at the extremity rounder.

Geese and ducks can be sexed manually at day-old; I prefer to wait till they are mature. Drakes, other than Muscovies, lose their voices before they grow their curly tails. With Muscovies, 'boys' are much larger than 'girls'. Handling them requires care—they scratch like cats.

Chinese geese are easy—the ganders have longer necks and more pronounced protuberances in front of the skull. The eyes appear to be rounder and larger. This same observation applies also to Emdens, Toulouse, and Romans. The voice is some guide providing one knows what to listen for and which bird is giving tongue. Geese have at least two distinct notes, the 'grumbling' or conversational tone and the cry of alarm or recognition. That of the male is higher and more piercing, designedly so. Nevertheless the safest way to ensure correct recognition of the sexes is by manipulation. It is astonishing that so few breeders have taken the trouble to learn. It is quite simple, as I have found out for myself.

My own technique is to grab the bird by the neck, up-end it with its head between my shins and my arms outside its wings, its back at right-angles to my front. With the finger and thumb of my left hand either side of its parson's nose I stretch its *cloaca*

66

backwards. With the first finger and thumb of the right hand on the opposite side of the orifice, I spread the vent right and left. From the age of five months old there should be no difficulty in exposing the male organ, however small. Inability to do so does not necessarily indicate that the bird is a female. None the less it usually means a reprieve!

Chapter 7

INCUBATION—THE ALTERNATIVES

To the present generation hatching and incubators are synonymous. The possibility that there is anything other than a machine is not even considered.

Incubators, it should be recalled, were invented to supplement the efforts of hens, not to replace them. Yet the substitute has come to be regarded as superior to the original; and if one is thinking in terms of hatcheries, of mass production and big business, one must agree that it is easier to attend to one cabinet incubator than to hundreds of broody hens.

Nevertheless there is ample scope for both machine and fowl in their respective circumstances, the one for quantity, the other for quality, the one for sale, the other for keeps. Yet the would-be poultry-keeper is so conditioned to the up-to-date that he ignores the down-to-earth. Besides, most men, at any rate, love messing about with gadgets and electricity. Not all of them welcome the idea of handling squawking hens. Women are different, in regard to machines at any rate; though few relish the prospect of being pecked and scratched.

It was a woman who first opened my eyes to the possibilities of natural hatching. She had had an unhappy experience with an oil-burning incubator which set itself on fire and incinerated all the embryos. She would never quite forget the stench. In her opinion hovers and brooders were just as dangerous. As she pointed out, in justification of her unorthodox views, a broody hen was perfectly capable of ruining a sitting of eggs in many and various ways, but she had never yet known one ignite.

Moreover her chickens compared more than favourably with most. And I had to agree.

Her houses, even by current standards, were pretty crude and usually overcrowded. Nevertheless her birds were healthy and lived to a ripe old age. That was in the 1930s at a time when high

68

mortality was beginning to engage the attention of the experts. It still does. Fowl paralysis for instance, about which little more is known now than then. Was it of any significance that pullets imported from Eire, mostly hen-hatched, were in demand for the very good reason that they stayed alive?

I was, against my better (?) judgment, impressed as my acquaintance with this lady ripened; as her flock continued to thrive, despite her archaic methods, I began investigating on my own account. Could there by any connection between large-scale incubation and this elusive expensive scourge?

It is known that chicks are very susceptible during their first few weeks of life. What more favourable environment can one envisage than an incubator or a brooder? If there is a 'carrier' chick its companions have every opportunity of picking up the infection. And the bigger the incubator the greater the chance of catching it. Is it a coincidence that the incidence of this disease has kept pace with the more general use of forced draught cabinet incubators? Another query: has the almost universal technique of loading eggs broad-end upwards any bearing on the problem? In a nest the eggs lie more or less on their sides; they are turned by the hen along their long axis, not end-over-end. I have a feeling that if Nature had designed eggs for hatching in modern incubators she would have made them spherical, rather than streamlining them for the convenience of the hen.

It may be contended that fowl paralysis is nothing more nor less than what was known in my youth as Layer's Cramp; that it is not a new manifestation at all; that it existed before incubators were invented; its incidence masked by the smallness of the clutch. If that be so one 'carrier' could only affect a dozen or so chicks. Which is no bad thing if the object is to breed only the best; a very good reason for my advocacy of the use of a broody rather than a machine; for breeding stock at any rate.

Consider the rival advantages. An incubator new is an expensive piece of equipment. It demands attention. A second-hand machine can be a positive menace. I have myself wasted hundreds of eggs and scores of hours on so-called bargains. If and when their vagaries have been successfully countered and the chicks duly hatched, more equipment in the shape of brooding appliances must be acquired. And some brooders are no more efficient than some incubators. For there is no law to prevent anyone from perpetrating some astounding contraption and exhibiting it at a show where it is bought by some optimist without its ever having reared a chick.

In the experienced hen one has, on the other hand, a proved hatcher and rearer. She knows when to turn the eggs, when to sit tight, when to sit light. To her problems of temperature, humidity, and ventilation do not exist. She is not subject to load-shedding nor power cuts. She has no belts to slip, no thermostats to fail. Moreover when she has produced the chicks she can rear them, and when she has taught them all she knows, she resumes egg production, if set in spring, at a time when big eggs are becoming scarce and valuable. Which is beyond the powers of any machine.

In fairness to the machine it cannot foul the nest nor peck the other machine's chicks to death. Nor can it infest the chicks with lice. On the other hand a rotten egg in a forced draught incubator has to be experienced to be believed. Under a hen it is relatively innocuous—in an incubator it is noxious. A machine is in use, on a breeding establishment at any rate, for months only, whereas a good hen is good for years; she is always contributing something. Yet to most people a broody hen is an unmitigated nuisance, to be isolated, pilloried or sold. How very short-sighted.

I have never claimed that natural hatching and rearing is the only method of retaining or achieving a disease-resistant flock. Similarly I have never claimed that my technique is the only possible one; but it appeals to me. Without it in fact I very much doubt if I could carry on in my present capacity of a spare-time breeder.

Not for me the text book advice to set crock eggs, to place the bird on the nest after thoroughly upsetting her, literally, by dusting her with insecticide; to lift her off and otherwise encourage her to do what comes naturally; to remove eggshells at hatching time, and generally to cause alarm, despondency and vexation. That is not my way, nor would I recommend it to anyone seriously considering the logical use of the hen.

I have set hens, and pullets, at all hours. In nine cases out of ten it is sufficient to show the hen the eggs through the back door. Even if the effect is not instantaneous and she walks over them to the far end, she usually returns quite soon. If she does not, no matter. At least she does not smash the eggs, as an unwilling parent would do if imprisoned in the orthodox coop.

There she is left to her own devices. Usually she stays put for a week or so. During the second week she shows an interest in food. In the last week she eats voraciously, until the nineteenth day when she gets down in real earnest. By then she may have eaten 3 lb of grain. I have never known one starve to death.

There are of course variations of the technique. One can lift her off each day if one cares to, and let her go back under her own power. For that matter, if one wants to be fussy, one can turn the eggs for her. A college-trained girl once deprecated my system on the ground that she was developing house-maid's knee—it was so much easier to turn eggs in an incubator! But I believe that a hen has nothing to learn from man on the subject of hatching eggs; any more than has one's granny on sucking them.

Some people prefer the tethering system; but I doubt if the hen does. In any case one needs a coop. And in my experience a run is very desirable too, more especially for the chicks' first week.

The purpose of the boarded sides is to give protection from the wind. I am all for bringing them up tough, but I see no point whatever in starting the process too soon. Normally I do not use a floor or litter, which is only kicked all over the place anyway. But when the ground is really damp a board floor is advisable (the framework should be below and run in the same direction as the coop is moved) otherwise one can expect trouble. There is no need for shutting up the coop at night, so no provision is made for it. The hen and chicks sleep virtually in the open air—in marked contrast to the average coop which is frequently rendered airtight by a close-fitting front. Again with the hen permanently behind bars, unless one is perpetually changing the bedding, the poor little waifs are inured to manure not of their own making. Whereas in my contraption it is most unusual to find the sleeping-quarters fouled.

Here then, protected from the sun, most of the rain and all of the wind, the chicks get a good start in life for the first vital week. If the hen is unusually aggressive one may have to keep her in and let the youngsters out. In this case one may prefer to have the front end of slats rather than boards. If so they are better placed horizontally; the drinking-vessels can conveniently be hung on them, progressively higher as the chicks increase in stature.

Generally, however, I prefer to let the hen accompany her brood. She keeps them together, teaches them what to eat and what to avoid, such as bees and wasps. Usually the first lesson consists of a dust bath and a taste of trace elements, grubs and the odds and ends not usually associated with modern menus. Her next effort, if more than one hen is at large, is as a rule an argument. Whatever the result, thereafter she abides by the decision. But let any optimist cat come her way! Never again. And when the chicks are old enough to fend for themselves they can, if need be, continue to sleep in this accommodating structure, on wet nights in the covered part, on hot nights in the run, until they are three months old. But I like to have them perching by then—the hen can teach them more conveniently than you or I.

So much for spring operations. Feeding can be simple. There is no need for expensive 'starter' mashes, crumbs or pellets, to be followed later by 'growers'. My normal food for baby chicks for the first week is oatmeal and skimmed milk, plus infertile eggs, if any. They are then given the same diet as the adults, whole wheat and a concentrate consisting mainly of cheese residues, plus a vital addition, raw greenfood, lawn mowings, lettuce, spinach or shredded cabbage. The grass in the chick enclosure is kept short. Young chicks are not bullocks. In case of drought I have gone to the trouble of watering the turf. In my submission greenfood is of the highest importance: it is cheaper than drugs and more efficacious. I would not like to have to rear chicks without it.

It is because autumn grass is not so palatable nor so plentiful and because salad crops are not usually so available, that feeding in autumn needs supplementing with extra milk, scalded biscuit meal, cod liver oil, or even for a while a concentrate supplemented with minerals and vitamins. Instead of letting the chicks range at a week old they should be restricted by a wire-covered enclosure for at least three weeks. Otherwise an energetic hen is certain to trail them through the saturated grass. I have known a feckless broody to settle down for the night with her brood in the snow.

A better environment than a grass run for atumn rearing is a vegetable garden, with access to the compost heap. Usually the earth is drier, there is shade and shelter, the lower buttons of brussels sprouts, the leaves of green turnips, self-sown causeway and meadow grass; and worms, larvae and grubs. Such a diet is better than one can buy. Later on the reader will find more detailed recommendations of suitable crops.

Chapter 8

SIMPLE FEEDING

My technique could scarcely be simpler. It is based on two facts
which have been established by far too many chicks, pullets, hens
and cockerels—not only mine—to be confuted by disbelievers. For,
strange though it may seem to those who rely on balanced rations,
my birds can not only grind their own cereals but can adjust their
own protein requirements for growth, maintenance and laying.

This discovery, naturally, has not been received with enthusiasm
by the dieticians and purveyors of mash and pellets. In the one
case their professional beliefs and teachings are affected, in the
other their profits. And I am completely unrepentant—so are my
fowls. They have subsisted, lived—some to a great age—laid and
bred on whole grain, mainly wheat, and a protein concentrate,
administered in separate containers, as much or as little as they
like. None has died of malnutrition nor an overdose of fish meal.
Nor have there been any complaints that my eggs have a fishy
taint.

That others have experienced such complaints is due not to the
system as such but to a shortage, maybe temporary, of greenfood
or grass; to a failure to appreciate that this system was designed
for range conditions, not for deep litter; that grain and protein
are not enough. In addition greenfood and sunlight, Vitamins A
and D in fact, are required, also certain minerals present in most
soils. It seems to have escaped general notice that fowls will, given
the opportunity, eat considerable quantities of earth.

There are snags, real snags. It has taken time and patience to
devise a self-feed hopper that is rat-, sparrow-, and weather-proof.
It has to be outside; or so I thought until recently. That meant
it has to be covered. That in turn necessitates, before it can be
replenished, the removal of the cover, in my case corrugated sheets,
and replacing them—a clumsy business.

I had three hoppers, self-closing, operated by the birds themselves. As they jump on the perch, linked to the hinged lid of the trough, the lid lifts and the birds can eat. When they jump off it comes down with a clang. Of the three hoppers, one I found derelict and had reconditioned, one I made from an oil-drum, the third, reputed to be weather-proof, I bought. By various means, extending the detachable roof, attaching side pieces and caulking seams, I improved it. But, in winter the mechanism still freezes and in summer the grain still sprouts.

One of my collaborators had been experimenting with oil-drums. He removed one end, and with it 1 in all round, to act as the lid. Round the base he made holes with a ½-in cold chisel at 3 in intervals, as near the rim as possible. To ensure a neat job it is advisable to pour in sand, to take the shock of the chisel, which is held with the cutting edge horizontal. Some metal is forced inwards at the top of the incision. This serves as a deflector and prevents the grain from flowing too freely.

The drum is suspended from a tripod or rafter. It is a source of nourishment and amusement for the fowls. They learn, the more inquisitive, to loosen the grain in the holes. The more diffident pick up what falls to the ground. This ingenious device has given excellent service even in intensive conditions, where, if open troughs are used, the birds fill their crops very quickly and have all the more time to savage each other.

Outside, the drum is not quite so successful. Water gets in via the holes and starts the sprouting process. Moreover sparrows somehow manage to hang on, upside down, and extract more than their share. Rats, so far as I am aware, cannot. Dust in the grain accumulates in the base and has to be removed, otherwise the fowls will starve. Even so, on a small scale, for the impecunious and less resourceful this drum hopper can be recommended, more particularly for young chicks. They rapidly learn the idea from the hen.

Another hopper, devised for pheasants, would seem equally suitable for poultry. It is a wooden box on legs, tapering from the top to the base. This consists of two layers of tightly stretched

FIG. 24. 'Help yourselves my dears'—week old chicks eating whole wheat from perforated drum

¼-in mesh wire netting. The birds stand below and peck upwards. If only it were made in perspex, one would not have to lift the lid to check the level of the contents. But this criticism applies so far as I know to all food containers.

Each of these feeding devices is known to work; each is suitable for the poultry-keeper on a domestic scale. As a potential professional I was not satisfied.

It is time-wasting to have to enter the enclosure to see if the hopper is empty. Could I insinuate a hopper in the end of a night ark, adjoining the main entrance, using the end wall as the back of the container? It only needed a board at an angle, with the lower edge ½ in clear of the base of the trough into which it directs the grain. It worked admirably. The chickens soon found it. So did the sparrows. I made a screen from wires hanging from the top edge of the pop-hole. That deterred the chickens for a time. The sparrows went below and up through the slats.

I have now geared the perch to the lid which is slightly heavier than the perch; light enough to be operated by one chicken. The other hoppers require the weight of a hen or several chicks. Even intelligent youngsters can be excused for not realizing immediately that they have to gang up for their food.

The latest model fits neatly inside the main entrance and takes up no more than 9 in floor space. It has a partition 3 in from one end separating the concentrate from the grain. To replenish it the roof is slid sideways, the contents of the sack decanted and the roof returned. One such hopper gives ample feeding space for at least fifty full-grown birds. With dry mash they would need six

FIG. 25. *Single-sided hopper in ark*

times as much—a considerable saving in capital expenditure.

Not everyone will approve of the hopper's location inside the ark. It restricts the number of fowls to 15, some of which may spend the night on the operating perch, to the benefit of the rats. Moreover, positioned thus, one has to wait until it is empty before tipping over the ark for manure removal. Even so there may conceivably be circumstances where the practice is justified and convenient, deep driving snow for instance, which can and does impede the free working of the mechanism. It requires very little snow on the perch to lift the lid of the trough. The obvious solution is to construct a scratching shed and park the hoppers during the worst of the weather.

FIG. 26. Double-sided grain hopper

Recently therefore I have been concentrating on the improvement of the double-sided hoppers. I have scrapped the wedges or cams which accelerate the lift of the hopper covers, and substituted rollers. These give a much smoother action. I have extended the wings and roof. This is now hinged, not sliding; again the result of winter experience. I have fitted rope handles for towing, and glass peepholes in the ends—a real time and transport saver. If only I could persuade some manufacturer to make these feeders of plastic sheet! I am sure they would be well rewarded. They must know that the average open hopper is a standing invitation to the rat, and deplorably wasteful of food, be it grain or mash.

Granted that if pellets or crumbs rather than mash are fed, much of what is hooked out of the hopper will be rescued from the litter, or in many instances the caked manure; but it must be pointed out that pellets cost more than mash, and at least one experimental station has recently proved to its own satisfaction that fowls lay more eggs on mash than on crumbs. So what? In any case under my system all manufacturing and mixing costs of the cereals are cut out.

The saving in feed costs is, literally, pounds per ton, even when grain is bought as required. Given storage facilities, rat-proof of course, one can buy forward when grain is at its cheapest. Unlike mash it does not grow stale. There is however no advantage in storing concentrates—they do not improve. The usual daily requirement of a laying fowl is only about $\frac{1}{2}$ oz. Obviously 1 cwt will last a small flock quite a while. It could become sour.

All this, to the orthodox, may seem incredible. Can hens really balance their rations? They can. There are however important provisos. There must be adequate greenfood. The chickens must be brought up on this diet from an early age. In some areas good oats, good barley may be more plentiful than wheat. If so what evidence I have is favourable e.g. (a) an arable farmer with a redundant tractor shed, 200 Leghorns, ample barley and greenfood, flock average over 200 eggs per bird as vouched for by the Packing Station (b) dairy farmer, 100 heavy cross pullets and more oats and silage than the cows could consume, reported he had never experienced such high egg production at such low cost. Unfortunately neither kept food records and neither used automatic hoppers; which in the case of oats was just as well, for the trough soon becomes clogged with husks.

Most of my collaborators fed wheat; some kept accurate records of food consumption and egg production. These figures provided me with material for reports and articles. The powers that were took notice. They were sceptical—where were the controls? I had none: it was hard enough to persuade busy farmers to record one lot. The statisticians demurred. I carried on acquiring further evidence. I was becoming an embarrassment. It was decided to lay on a controlled experiment, grain ad lib plus protein and greenfood, shell and grit, versus dry mash of similar analysis.

Of the five sites selected only one provided more or less free range. This turned out to be so heavily infected with intestinal worms that the project was abandoned. The second was virtually a deep litter house densely stocked with access to an open littered yard. Here the participants, light hybrids, spent their waking hours laying and murdering each other. Actually their production compared very favourably with the best. A somewhat similar outfit less densely populated, duplicated, showed one control flock, i.e. mash fed, appreciably better than the grain-fed, the other mash lot rather worse. It was later admitted that the greenstuff provided averaged less than half of what I had stipulated, viz. 14 lbs per 100 fowls per day.

The fourth flocks were housed in lightly stocked folding units on beautiful grass. As one might expect the grain fed birds beat the mash fed control. In this case the statisticians pointed out rather unkindly, that the numbers involved were barely significant.

The fifth outfit was hastily withdrawn when the head man was faced by a fishy-tasting egg for breakfast. The birds were, I gathered, a pretty poor lot and several had already died before the dénouement. They were accommodated in folds on, I was later told, a worn out weedy pasture. In such circumstances grain and protein is inadequate for satisfactory production. That has been frequently proved—greenness does not necessarily indicate palatable grass. I can cite two outstanding examples, one docks and black grass, the other agrostis, (creeping bent) 4 in deep, quite inedible.

This matter of evil smelling eggs is puzzling. I have known cases of birds in cages fed as much as 30% of fishmeal, with no complaints; also of birds fed no fishmeal at all, at least one of which produced an occasional "fishy egg". Can it be due to the retention of the egg in the cloaca by a hen going out of production, her last egg for instance prior to broodiness?

There are other foodstuffs available in some districts, good swill, 'pudding' (concentrated house scraps), bread, for instance. If these are given in large quantities to birds on a so-called balanced ration without any compensating additions it becomes hopelessly unbalanced. The birds put on weight and egg production is adversely affected; not so on my system—the birds will still maintain their own individual correct proportions.

For it must be realized that a flock is composed of individuals. Who is to say that all birds must have, say, 17 per cent of protein? To the non-laying bird or one producing only the occasional egg it is too much. On the other hand a bird laying every day requires more. In the one case her kidneys may be affected, in the latter she will draw on her reserves and lose condition.

A further reason for feeding grain whole, rather than pulverized, has recently been advanced by the veterinarians—it induces an acid condition of the digestive tract which is inimical to such intestinal organisms as coccidiosis, blackhead and typhoid.

One 'expert' who ought to know better holds the opinion that to feed greenfood is to affect the protein ratio. Bearing in mind that a hen is not likely to eat much more than 2 oz of greenstuff a day, that most of it is water, the risk of protein poisoning would not appear alarming. Even so good short grass is rich in protein. There is ample evidence that in spring the consumption of concentrate is very low, well below the normal $\frac{1}{3}$ oz. One of my friends with an inquiring mind once kept a small flock for a whole year on wheat, grass and vegetables. The average was 159 eggs per bird. The following year as hens, they were given in addition grain balancer pellets at the rate of 1 : 4 of wheat. Their production rose to 188 eggs apiece. It was noted that many of the pellets were wasted. It would appear that the cost of the additional protein was justified.

To revert to greenfood. One of the factors overlooked by the modern exponent of *ad lib* dry mash or pellet feeding is the lack of variety. It is conceivable that hens become sick and tired of the same dull diet. Even wheat and fish-meat can pall. It is not surprising that my birds spend so much time grazing, scratching and excavating. Actually most days I give them a little something extra.

The best way to feed oats, barley or maize is as a scratch feed in the least palatable grass, and woe betide the bird that does not come a-running. In a drought or frosty weather I take the trouble to soak, boil or steam an extra feed of grain. Surplus beans, bread, apples and house scraps are all welcome and there is no fear whatever of upsetting their calculations. I doubt in fact if it is necessary to offer protein *ad lib*. Another of my disciples gives fish-meal twice a week, Tuesdays and Fridays actually. So far as I know there is no religious significance! Egg production is perfectly satisfactory. Had it not been she would have changed her technique.

There are alternatives to fish-meal: meat and bone; various proprietary supplements containing vitamins and minerals, some less palatable than others; soya-bean and earthnut-meal are usually cheaper than animal protein. Both are relished by poultry, but if used should be given in addition to, not instead of, fish- or meat-meal. There are also several milk and cheese by-products in the form of meals or semi-solid blocks. All these have been tried on my much-enduring fowls and all have been readily consumed.

One final observation, the answer to which no dietician has so far supplied. Why is it that the manure of fowls on my diet is compact, black and white, whereas on mashes and pellets much of it is disgustingly frothy, jaundiced and viscous?

I have no reservation about self-choice feeding for chicks and layers on good grass. For fattening cockerels in similar circumstances I am not so sure. I have a feeling that they would put on weight better if segregated and fed boiled grain, barley or wheat especially.

How do other species of poultry react to this system?

Turkey raisers have been practising the technique with success for years. I see no reason why turkey breeding stock should not sort things out for themselves equally successfully. I hesitate to recommend the system for laying ducks on free range, though it would not surprise me to hear that they can cope just as sensibly as fowls. And why not? They have, I believe, more intelligence. So too with geese. My method is to administer the grain in water, for ducks about 4 oz each, for geese rather more. In early spring, when the grass is poor and worms are not available, a little fish- or meat-meal in the water is desirable. Good swill and soaked bread if obtainable cheaply can also be recommended. Pellets in my experience should not be fed *ad lib.* I recall an incident when an enterprising salesman called on me one evening. Would I care to try his pellets on my fowls? They had gone to bed. So I gave the sample to the geese. Next morning the senior, heavier and greedier goose was floating upside down on the pond. I assumed that the pellets had swollen in her crop and choked her.

Sometimes one forgets to provide oyster shell and insoluble grit. Without the former they will not lay any eggs. Omit the grit and they will bury their faces deep in the earth in search of pebbles or flints, more particularly where the ground is soft. Moral, move the drinking-bowl from time to time. For reasons best known to themselves geese are very fond of rotten timber.

83

Chapter 9

ESTABLISHING A STRAIN
AND AVOIDING DISEASE

Most people would agree that pedigree breeding is a fulltime job, requiring constant attention to trapnests and incubators. Yet it can be done on a small scale with neither, and with the owner away for the greater part of most days. It is true that on occasions there may be some element of doubt as to which hen laid which egg. With pullets there is the additional hazard of their visiting a former or unauthorized husband.

Hens, generally, are more disciplined, or resigned, in some cases too heavy, perhaps, to fly or climb. I have one exceptional hen from whom all my birds are descended. She still has a roving eye. Her eggs are now elongated and thin of shell. She remains on the strength as my best broody. For six successive years she produced annually three broods. More recently she has been satisfied with two.

Fortunately many hens lay distinctive eggs; even sisters exhibit subtle differences, in shape, size, colour or markings. They vary a little from day to day. Almost always they grow paler towards the end of a clutch. By observation at weekends with only two or three hens in an enclosure, it is not difficult to identify with a high degree of accuracy most of the eggs laid.

All my hens destined for breeding carry large coloured plastic wing-tabs located by press studs or, more cheaply by bent wire, in the web of the wing. The tabs are triangular in shape and bear large digits easily visible from a distance. The idea was borrowed, with acknowledgement, from a Belgian breeder nearly forty years ago. It took seventeen years to persuade an English maker to produce it and the conservative English breeder to adopt it. Recently I was advised by a young geneticist to try it!

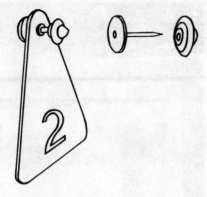

FIG. 27. Wing tab and press stud, fixed near lower edge of wing and hanging clear of hackle feathers

My trapnest was also copied from a Belgian design. It is very easy to make. Materials required are plasterers' laths, offcuts of board or matching, a few nails and webbing, or gents' discarded braces. The horizontal laths are sandwiched top and bottom between vertical laths forming grooves, up and down which slide beheaded nails driven into the lower extremities of the lower board. This is attached, accurately but loosely, by two parallel strips of webbing, to the upper board, which hangs by the webbing from the upper horizontal lath. The offcuts are about 10 in by 4–5 in, giving an overall measurement of the trapnest front of rather less than 1 ft square. To set it one raises the lower board high enough to allow the entrance of a hen. As her back touches the boards, now at an angle, they straighten out. The hen is inside and cannot escape. On releasing her the egg is marked with her number and stored prior to setting.

This matter of storage is important, more especially where only a few hens are involved. With the large-scale operator setting twice a week the problem scarcely arises—eggs are bound to be fresh. With one hen, for instance, it will take her a fortnight at

FIG. 28.   Trap-nest—front

least to complete a clutch. Such eggs must be treated with care if they are to hatch. Years ago, during spring, with no frosts, I proved to my own satisfaction that the best results came from eggs resting on their sides on the ground. To adopt this technique on a large scale would be impractical at any time, and fatal in cold weather.

Three factors are involved: temperature, humidity and turning. I have used a wooden box containing sand or earth with a well-fitting lid. Turning is laborious. Better is a shallow box divided longitudinally by rods or wires, one track per hen or mating, along which the eggs can be gently rolled on their sides, the whole covered by a piece of dry towelling. Easiest of all is an old-fashioned incubator with a manually operated self-turning tray,

FIG. 29. Trap-nest—set

with ventilation holes sealed and water in the moisture trays. Where only a few eggs are saved, a hatching egg-box, with felt-lined compartments, serves admirably. It is held on its side, not on the base, and reversed each day.

With all these devices the air space at the broad end of the egg increases but slowly. Very little humidity is lost. On a larger scale, where storage room is at a premium, they can be held in ordinary egg trays in cases, in an insulated shed heated in winter by a greenhouse stove with a bucket of water on top. In summer water is poured over the floor and evaporates, cooling and moistening simultaneously.

I have set individual hens on a dozen of their own eggs and hatched as many as ten good chicks. On occasion I have allowed a

hen to make her own arrangements in a hedge. It is as well, howeve
to see that no other hen contributes; otherwise there can be no
guarantee, among the offspring, of authentic pedigree. On a small
scale, hatching only from a very few hens and only one male, the
chicks can be identified by toe-slits. It is not cruel. The operation
is simple. One takes the chick in one hand, sets its feet down flat
on top of the coop and presses the point of a sharp knife against
the web. The incision should not be deep— $\frac{1}{8}$ in is more than
enough. A single cut can be made in one of four places. The total
possible combinations are fifteen.

These marks remain for life. They do not, of course, give any
indication of date of hatch. For that one can use coloured leg
bands which have to be replaced as the chicks grow. Nowadays
it is customary to use wing bands of the bent pin type numbered
and/or lettered. Where chicks are raised under hens it is not
advisable to attach wing bands until the chicks are a week old. I
have known instances of the youngsters being caught up in the
hen's feathers—very alarming to both parties. In practice I find a
convenient time is when transferring them from the coop in
which they were hatched to their new quarters in the rearing
enclosure. Incidentally, to catch them without losing one's temper
it is as well to remove the hen first, then to restrict the chicks to
the run part of the combined coop by a spare rear end.

To revert to pedigree technique, it helps if one keeps two
breeds, of different plumage and egg colour. Even from an older
hen in spring it is reasonable to expect five or six eggs in a week.
In my case the white chicks are from a hen of my own strain, the
black ones from one of the Marans, of which I keep a few for
testing purposes. Let me explain.

My birds are white. Some of them when mated with grey or
black Recessives, throw all white. These are known as Dominant.
Others throw half white, half black. These are known as
Heterozygous. To prove dominance it is necessary to hatch ten
chicks, all white, none black, from a white—black mating. It is not
difficult to imagine the disappointment and frustrations in attemp
ing to establish the dominance of every individual female of good

physique and productivity, and of every male of outstanding characteristics and the right breeding; all this without trapnets and, until recently, an incubator.

My few Dominants are all descended from a hen and cock, sister and brother, and the same hen with one of her sons. Needless to say many of the eggs failed to hatch; some of the chicks proved difficult to rear. Such as did survive are of course all Dominant. Mated to Heteros they throw all whites, half of which are Dominant. But they all have to be proved; that means more mating with Marans, more saving of eggs, more waiting for broody hens, more farming out with collaborators, more marking of eggs with indelible pencil, transferring some from one broody hen to another, standing by, so to speak. Sometimes she stands up!

Why go to all this trouble? Why Dominant? For two reasons; one, because the value of the birds for crossing purposes is greatly enhanced. Some of our most prolific varieties are coloured and have yellow legs. By using one of my males the progeny is white all over, plumage, skin and legs; with consequent increase in value of the cockerels, and, ultimately, of the hens. Nor will their egg production be worsened—my birds are quite good layers.

The other reason was more personal. I regarded the establishment of a dominant strain as a challenge. I could have cheated and acquired existing broiler stock, with all their weaknesses, yellow, willow, blue legs and, when crossed, an astonishing variety of plumage colours. I preferred to use my own basic strain founded in the first instance on Malines, the Belgian table bird of exceptional conformation, with an infusion of Marans, a French breed, which lays very attractive brown eggs and matures early. Incidentally both these varieties have a reputation for hardiness and relative freedom from present-day fashionable diseases. The females too are unsophisticated enough to take seriously the job of motherhood.

In reserve is a wartime 'utility' incubator. It was given me because it would not hatch. Its owner was emphatic—if I brought it back he would throw it out—and me after it! I accepted the challenge.

I conquered its vagaries eventually. It took me three years; to be accurate, three hatching seasons. I lost count of the eggs it spoilt and the hours I stood by, watching the temperature creeping up, and hoping and waiting for the cut-out to operate. Then waiting and hoping for the temperature to stop dropping.

It was a deplorable job. Nothing fitted. The removable front leaked hot air at every corner. The push-rod fouled its tube; the stirrup carrying the capsule was off centre; the milled adjusting nut was loose on the thread. I added a fibre lock nut. The thermometer was 2° out.

I made a stirrup which prevented the capsule from wobbling. It was sufficiently out of line to compensate for the out-of-vertical push-rod tube. I greased the rod, lubricated and re-bushed the cut-out mechanism. After every adjustment I waited and watched.

Then I made a real discovery. The floorboards had parted—not a lot, but enough to affect the ventilation. I lagged the whole machine, top, bottom, sides, back and front, with hardboard, except for the vents. There was some improvement. A few eggs, salvaged from a temperamental broody, duly hatched. They must have had strong germs!

It was still erratic, still prone to run up to 106 °F, and to linger around 100 °F. I started all over again, this time with the capsule. The peg below was a good fit in the stirrup. The hollow in the top in which the base of the push-rod rested was suspiciously bright. Could the rod be wobbling? If so, how to stop it? I found a small bush, slightly larger in diameter than the rod, and fixed it with plastic glue in the centre of the capsule. And that cured it, completely and successfully.

My incubator now helps. After eighteen or nineteen days one hen's eggs are left under the broody, the rest are transferred to the machine. If more than one hen's eggs are involved they have to be hatched separately, in muslin bags, cardboard boxes, or special pedigree wire cages. When they are hatched—if they hatch—the chicks must be toe-punched before returning to the hen.

One needs a wing-band record book. The numbers are set out serially on the left side of the page. Opposite each number is the mother's wing-tab and that of the cock. In another column is the date. The rest of the page is left vacant for notes, of progress or lack of it, sickness perhaps, even death in some cases, sale or disposal, and for the outstandingly excellent, its adult number. The wing-band book is the vade-mecum of the breeder.

Another record book contains hatching results, details of eggs set, when, infertiles, dead in shell, weak chicks, toe-punch marks of those that do hatch. For testing eggs I use an electric torch. It helps if some of the light is concentrated by a metal shield, a round tobacco-tin lid for instance, with an oval hole cut away, or a few inches of rubber tube. Actually with experience one can pick out the infertiles by touch. They lose heat rapidly by comparison with fertile eggs. One has only to hold them against one's eyelid to sense the difference.

Nowadays I try to set three hens at a time. In this way if many eggs are infertile one or two hens can be used again. For some cocks are not very active in the early spring; some cockerels are distinctly selective; some in fact refuse to mate with hens of a different colour. Moreover if the hatch is only reasonably successful, one or two hens should be able to cope with those chicks that do hatch.

On a small scale one can get away with the hatching and wing-band books and one's memory. As one's operations extend and memory begins to fail, one needs an individual record card, more particularly where close inbreeding is practised. I devised such a card forty years ago. On the front it has columns for all the usual requirements, number, parents, production, brief summary of hatching results with different mates, other information such as weight, broodiness, or other characteristics. On the reverse side is an extended pedigree chart, mother and her parents, father and his, as far back as one cares to go. In practice two, or at most three, generations are ample.

With these cards the problem of the selection of breeding pens is simplified. One can see at a glance how close is the relationship between individuals. Cousins for instance can be grouped. One avoids what I regard as a dangerous mating, brother and sister. It is not necessary to wade through page after page of a ledger. When a bird is no longer alive or fit to breed the card is discarded. It is easier than searching through masses of records belonging to long dead birds.

I can, if need be, trace all my stock back to the hen I acquired in 1945. Several times the strain has nearly petered out. It may be asked why I have not bought or exchanged cockerels. Frankly I would not dare—I have seen some of the results of outcrossing, in terms of paralysis especially. My practice is to give to a fellow poultry-keeper operating on my old-fashioned lines a surplus cock and to get back in return one or two of his daughters. If, as has been the case of late, the cock is Dominant and his mates are Recessive, all the progeny are Heteros. If the selected daughters are good enough they are mated, as pullets, to a proved Dominant cock If their progeny are satisfactory and they and their offspring live, lay and thrive, then and only then are their Dominant daughters brought into the cockerel-producing pen. Meantime once he has been proved Dominant a son of a Dominant—Hetero mating, in most cases a nephew, is mated with Dominant hens of the pure line. In this manner there is a gradual infusion of carefully screened fresh blood.

I have mentioned paralysis, which is I believe one of the greatest scourges among present ills; the other is infectious bronchitis. Neither affects my stock. Are they immune to the former and resistant to the latter by reason of their open air start in life? Twice in the last nine years I have experienced losses among pullets from hens not of my own breeding. In each case the progeny that has survived, mated to one of my own males, has thrown perfectly satisfactory offspring. In one case I acquired a sitting of eggs from which I selected two pullets, one of which, mated to a home-bred male, failed to breed. Her sister threw nine pullets; eight died or were killed in varying stages of paralysis, blood blisters or blindness The sole survivor produced my first two Dominants, also a Hetero, and a Recessive. The two Dominants, male and female, are now pensioned off. None of their progeny has shown the slightest indication of weakness.

Just how far these gratifying results are due to acquired immunit induced by my methods of hatching and rearing and feeding I do not know. The fact remains that they are true.

Not everyone wants to trapnest and fill up record cards; though if improvement is desired I know of no alternative. One can, however, maintain the standard with very little effort, and relatively small numbers, say four breeding-pens each of ten hens and a cockerel—maybe fewer. It is assumed of course that it is a good flock. One would be ill-advised to start inbreeding with poor stock.

The first stage is to select the most promising cockerel from each family and to mate him to the surviving hens. One of them may be his mother. If she is a good hen there is no reason to fear for the quality of the progeny. If all the other hens are her own sisters, there is still no need to worry about too close inbreeding— aunt X nephew has in my experience proved very successful.

Next year some younger hens will be included in the pen, again headed by a cockerel, never a cock. This way, by keeping a generation between the sexes, there is no fear of mating brother and sister. One can go on repeating this system for three or four or more generations before hatchability is affected.

Meanwhile the same procedure is being followed with the other three pens. All chicks are of course toe-punched to their respective blood lines, 1, 2, 3 or 4. Their year of birth is indicated either by coloured leg ring or, better still, wing-tab. For in every generation there are the determined wanderers—frequently the best layers, and leg rings pick up mud.

Not that the odd bird in the wrong enclosure will seriously affect the breeding results. It is not even essential to keep to the four-pen system, though that way one gets warning, by an increase in the proportion of dead embryos, that the time has come for a change of blood—an infusion from one of the other three strains.

Flock mating is even simpler. The mathematical odds against choosing four brothers from a few score of promising cockerels are astronomical. And the chances against any individual's mating exclusively with one closely related female must be equally remote. Yet I would prefer individual matings as offering some measure of improvement. One strain for instance might after a few generations show outstanding characteristics lacking in one or all of the others. Just as another might develop a weakness that can be strengthened from within the flock.

Whichever method is selected there will be a gratifying uniformity in a very short time. More important, the value of the birds will be enhanced. When in due course the venture is given up, the flock should be very valuable. For the number of closed flocks is very small. Sooner or later modern mass producers will be glad of healthy fresh blood lines.

Disease is not inevitable. Yet it is very easy to acquire. Borrowed broody hens for instance are a frequent source of infection—bacillary white diarrhoea for example. That happened to my flock many years ago when I acquired ex-broodies from a gamekeeper. It could have been typhoid, pest, paralysis and all kinds of unpleasant ailments; more recently I imported scaly leg via a borrowed broody which she passed on to her chicks. My remedy is crude but effective, neat creosote.

My other bane is gapes. I am not certain how my ground became infested. I rather suspect some chicks that I had farmed out and brought home half reared; though that same spring I acquired a pair of geese. The following season I lost a good many promising chickens. My immediate reaction was to dig a trench at the foot of the bank adjoining the baby chick enclosure and to keep the grass mown. I also acquired a supply of garlic pills. I could have dressed the land with mowrah-meal and destroyed all the earthworms, the intermediate hosts, but I prefer the garlic treatment, one pill per gallon of drinking-water. It is the only medicine I use.

For dogs, goats and geese it has the reputation of being a gentle vermifuge. I know one poultry-breeder who further contends that it prevents coccidiosis, another that it keeps his turkeys clear of blackhead; though for both these ailments I pin my faith to green-food and grain. Unquestionably garlic is a tonic—some claim an antibiotic. Certainly it has justified my simple trust on several occasions when after a couple of pills poor unthrifty birds have improved out of all recognition, put on weight and become useful members of the flock. It could be that they harboured more than their share of worms.

In this connection some varieties of intestinal worms require intermediate hosts, snails, slugs, earthworms or flies, before they affect chickens. The easiest way to deal with them is to run a few ducks over the rearing ground; unlike geese, ducks are carnivorous.

I have known, not on my establishment, cases of recurrent coccidiosis where drugs have proved useless; persistent colds that have failed to react to chemicals. Spectacular success has attended a course of garlic pills. They cost about a penny each from most pet stores. I now grow my own garlic, one segment or clove, a couple of inches deep, 6 in apart, planted preferably in October for maximum yield, though March gives quite a good crop.

The standard dose is one clove per gallon of water. There is no point in throwing it into an open bowl—it floats. One should cut it up small, when the particles will sink to the bottom. If the drinker is the orthodox chick fount the whole clove is inserted. If an open drinker is used I put the clove in a tin, perforated, with a lid. So far even my ingenious fowls have failed to remove it.

Chapter 10

FARMING IN MINIATURE

I do not propose to spend my gratuity on expensive housing. I regard land as a much better investment. For a few thousand pounds, in agricultural districts, one can obtain a house much bigger and better built than a suburban villa, frequently with good outbuildings and several acres. That is what I am seeking. When I find it I shall do on a larger scale what I have been doing in miniature for years. The difference will be in degree only.

That is my intention now as I write, before retiring. Not everyone will be so ambitious. Pensioners do not get any younger or fitter. What is practicable at sixty-five is exacting at seventy, barely possible at seventy-five, and out of the question at eighty. It follows then that one's plans must be flexible and designed to allow a gradual reduction of effort without letting the land grow derelict. That means in effect putting it back to grass, either for letting or grazing, as one's poultry stocks are reduced.

The layout will be, so far as practicable, identical with that evolved over forty years ago, what I call the 'strip' system. Each enclosure will have its counterpart fore and aft of the poultry house, in my case the same night ark which has served me so well. The partitions will be transferred from one static fence line to the other. To avoid the labour of reversing ark and shelter to give the birds access to the rested enclosure the ends of the static fence can be moved sideways. The resting strip will then be cut for hay or cropped. The old bugbear of stale, poultry-sick land will be avoided indefinitely.

Just so long as I remain reasonably active I shall hope to make the best possible use of the manure by returning it to the soil to grow food for myself, for sale, and/or to feed back to the fowls. The ideal is a crop attractive to humans and palatable to fowls.

FIG. 30. Fence batten moved to alternative position

For there is bound to be a proportion not suitable for sale or consumption in the home. In the right circumstances, a skilled gardener might care to grow calabrese for instance, cauliflowers, or even luxury crops which may spring to the mind of more experienced horticulturists.

What to grow, and how much, depends on several factors, the number of birds in relation to the acreage, the degree of intensivism in fact; the activity of the owner and the extent of his mechanization; the type of soil, the slope, drainage, elevation, climate. One cannot be dogmatic; but in my experience I believe that the most flexible and accommodating crop is cabbage. It is easy to grow and to transplant. There is very little waste. With generous manuring some varieties yield up to 30 tons an acre. Such an area would in theory provide 2 oz per day of greenfood for 1,500 fowls for a year. Naturally one would not plant all one variety at the same time, and not everyone likes cow cabbage. Fortunately poultry do.

There are of course alternatives: maize, lucerne, clover, rye, barley, wheat, oats, all of course cut green; on a large establishment a forage harvester would seem indicated. Silage made from

LAYOUT FOR 3 ACRE FIELD

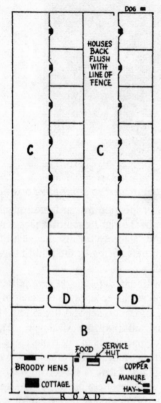

FIG. 31.

Layout for 3 acre field
A = Administration
B = Chick enclosure
C = Resting pens
D = Occupied pens

98

FIG. 32. *To provide access to resting enclosure one has only to move fence batten*

young grass will serve in winter but a good deal is wasted. The textbook advises caution in its use by reason of the possibility of its causing green yolks, but that has not been my experience.

These suggestions are for the large-scale producer with little land, such as those in Belgium and Australia where poultry-keepers are still prepared to utilize rather than burn manure. Incidentally an increasing number of egg producers in Victoria are feeding whole grain, wheat, meat-meal and greenfood.

For the small man such as I, with a large garden, a small family and several dozen hens and chickens, it is only necessary to grow rather more than the household is likely to eat. In my garden I always grow onions, chives, shallots, and Welsh onions for the young chicks. For use during a drought there is spinach beet, Swiss chard, lettuce and chicory, and for the winter in addition to cabbage, sprouts, broccoli, the purple variety in particular, thousand head, Scotch kale, green turnips and kohlrabi. So far I have not grown comfrey, though I understand that despite its hairy leaves poultry like it. On occasion I have

99

acquired silage from a neighbouring farmer.

I would not care to keep breeding hens without greenfood. Nor would I care to garden without manure.

Cropping, if my grassland management should by any chance necessitate it, will not include cereals. With narrow strips cross cultivations are not practicable. One is restricted to row crops, potatoes, roots and brassicas, followed immediately by direct reseeding; in the autumn after early potatoes, in early spring after kale or winter cabbage. In either case the land should be clean enough, with nothing more than a light harrowing.

Just exactly what kind of cultivator to use depends on the land. There are strong advocates of the rotary type. On heavy land a plough may be necessary. In most circumstances however there would seem no need for both. A tractor plough can usually be hired. If the land is infested with couch or bindweed a rotary cultivator can be expected to spread it.

Given a good seed bed however and high germination, the grass will kill both. I have achieved a first-class take on chalky clay, packed solid by generations of hens; not a blade of grass, nothing but plantains, wild radish, a few vetches and convolvulus. The first cultivation with a rotary hoe nearly separated my arms from my torso.

After two or three weeks I raked up the rubbish and the biggest flints and went over it again with the machine. The final seed bed was achieved with a wooden hay rake, an excellent tool. I then waited for the weather to break. It usually does in August. The seeds went in, the land was raked across the miniature drills, and down came the rain. So too, when it stopped raining, did the birds of the air. Whereupon I installed pegs and thread, feathers on sticks and a scarecrow. Had I possessed a roller I would have used it. But the result could not have been much better. I might have dressed the seeds with paraffin but did not. Maybe I was lucky.

Reseeding is, on the drier side of England at any rate, best carried out in the late summer, but not later than mid-September. At that time most of the annual weeds have finished seeding, and, even should there be little or no rain, heavy dews can be expected. The grass seeds should not burn up, as they frequently do in spring. Nor should they be smothered in weeds.

As to seed mixtures, they need not be complex nor expensive. The most palatable grasses are timothy, preferably S50, cocksfoot S143, meadow fescue, meadow grasses, smooth and rough-stalked, and *Italian* rye-grass. I would never dream of sowing perennial rye-grass. It may be good for bullocks; poultry will only eat it if none of the more attractive species are available. Clovers are of no interest to chickens until they come into lay. Yet they are an essential part of the sward.

A very useful mixture, particularly in dry areas, is 12 lb Cocksfoot S143 and 1 lb wild white clover per acre. One or 2 lb of chicory per acre can be relied on to provide grazing but if the intention is to save it for hay omit the chicory. I have the keenest recollection of trying to cut it with a scythe. By the time I moved in it was head high. I could not clear the site; and when I had succeeded it would not burn. A little yarrow helps but does not contribute much bulk. On heavy land timothy S50 at the rate of 10 lb per acre can be safely recommended. In such circumstances clover can be omitted—it will come in of its own accord. So will rough-stalked meadow grass.

Cultivations need not be deep. Sowing can be by hand or fiddle, followed by a brush harrow and rolling. If no roller is available, geese will do the job just as well with their great feet. Laying pullets should on no account be allowed on to young seeds until they have rooted deeply. Moulting hens are not so destructive, nor are young stock, though they may make dust-baths. If there is a good take of chicory and the weather is wet I have on occasion broken my own rule and let laying pullets on after six weeks, under observation, rather than waste the chicory which is very much to their liking. Once it has been consumed the birds should be removed.

For a hurried job in the autumn, after main-crop potatoes for instance, 10 lb Italian rye-grass and 3 lb rape will provide winter grazing. Geese will fatten on it. The rye-grass will come again after

Christmas and continue to withstand heavy grazing; then when it
seeds it can either be further grazed or ploughed in—most
accommodating in fact, and cheap. Another cheap catch crop is
rye, though more suitable for turkeys than fowls, also hardy
green turnips.

Turkeys intrigue me. As a youngster one of my jobs was to
round up the poults when thunderstorms were about. For rain
and lice, not blackhead, were, in our experience, the greatest
menaces. The poults were of course hatched and reared by hens.
Their food was hard-boiled egg, chopped greenfood, nettles,
spinach, dandelions, skimmed milk and boiled grain. Later they
roamed the night pasture and the aftermath and gleaned the oat-
fields. They did not die. Sometimes they developed runny noses.
That was our fault for shooing them off the roof of the cartshed
and insisting on their sharing a stuffy henroost with the fowls.
They would have been perfectly safe from the fox on the ridge
tiles and would not have caught colds. Looking back, our main
problem was infertility. For it was not our practice to use a
young male and scrap him after a few months' use. Sometimes
he was kept too long and became too heavy for his mates; also
hens, not immature poults. Nowadays the practice is to use
young females exclusively, just because they lay more eggs. Their
mates are young stags, selected for rate of growth and conformation. Both sexes are scrapped after the breeding season.
It is exceptional to use really mature birds. Not, one would
imagine, the best way to establish a superior strain; many so-called
breeders are in fact simply out-crosses and artificial inseminators.

If and when I take up the breeding of turkeys I shall adopt the
same technique as has served me so well with hens. I shall establish
a strain. I know where I shall obtain my foundation stock—from a
lady who keeps old stags, old hens and hatches the natural way.
She has to my knowledge experienced the results of using other
people's stags. Fortunately her pure line remains unsullied.

Housing, once the poults are feathered, is not essential although
it may be necessary to fence against foxes and dogs. Given the
opportunity turkeys prefer trees. I know one farmer's wife who

rears hers on the lawn. The coops are gradually moved nearer to an ancient pear tree outside her bedroom. Her husband keeps a shotgun handy.

Others erect apex perches in wire netting enclosures, taking care to leave the top 2 ft of the fence floppy and hanging outwards. Fairy lights flicking on and off are another deterent. In the U.S.A., where presumably paraffin is cheaper, naked flares are placed at intervals of 50 ft around the sleeping birds.

As to whether perches, and for that matter nests, are necessary is arguable. There is no argument as to the desirability from the point of view of health and saving in foodstuffs, of roughage in the form of greenery. The best turkey-breeder I ever knew, with hundreds of turkeys on five acres only, used to take them for a walk every day. He went in front, they followed. Nothing came amiss, potato haulm, blackberries, nettles, docks, everything in fact but red beet tops. He had some difficulty in keeping them off his neighbour's seeds. They will clear a one-year ley as neatly as a herd of cows. A seeds mixture suitable for chickens is not to be advised—there is not nearly sufficient bulk. Instead I would suggest Italian rye-grass and broad red clover, say 10 lb of each per acre. Autumn-sown rye gives excellent winter grazing. Winter oats or wheat can be grazed to advantage, without damage, as turkeys do not scratch. If there is nothing else, silage.

About geese I have mixed feelings. They are undeniably attractive, but except in wartime not particularly profitable. If one can hatch them the baby goslings find a ready market. The best incubators I know are Muscovy ducks. But they are very temperamental. Only two makes of cabinet incubators can hatch goose eggs. In each case the trays are horizontal. So too are those in old-fashioned table-type machines. With second-hand hot water incubators I found that frequent turning was essential, three, bettter still four times a day, and a temperature of $105°-106°$, the thermometer bulb level with the top of the eggs, there seemed no advantage in spraying the eggs.

Housing for geese is a waste of money. They will cheerfully sleep in the snow. The problem with nests is to find them. Muscovy

ducks are just as hardy, and just as crafty in hiding their eggs.
Given the opportunity they too will sleep in trees or on the roof.
Laying ducks are more domesticated and respond to housing, but
it need not be elaborate. One has the choice of a structure tall
enough to allow the attendant to walk inside to collect the eggs,
or so designed as to provide access from outside through the roof.
For an Aylesbury breeding-pen of a drake and five or six ducks a
lean-to shed 4 ft X 3 ft X 3 ft high is perfectly adequate. My night
ark with a ramp attached to the front, an extra pop-hole and a
partition, will house two units. The best litter is wood chips,
though wheat straw if reasonably priced is a good substitute.
Whichever is chosen plenty is needed, for ducks are prone to
rheumatism.

One by-product of both geese and Muscovies is worth
considering. I mean *pâté*. There is no secret, no magic. It is
however by no means a pleasant job. The geese do not like
being crammed twice a day with cooked white maize. Nor does
the crammer enjoy the performance. The price of the finished
article was however so tempting that I conceived the idea of
starting a peasant industry. I even went to the trouble of importing
genuine Toulouse goslings. Recently I have learnt that any
variety will do with the exception of Chinese. Subsequently I
found out that un-crammed goose and Muscovy duck livers make
delectable *pâté*. For anyone interested I append the recipe.

Pâté

    1 lb goose liver.
    ½ lb fresh bacon or pork with fat.
    2–3 onions.
    1 clove garlic.
    A little thyme, parsley, and a bay leaf.
    Put in a pan with salt and pepper, just cover with
    water and simmer for half an hour. Pass through a
    fine sieve, add truffles and a small glass of Madeira.
    Mix to a paste. Place in glass jar, cover with melted
    lard.

My favourite breed is the Roman, for the very good reason that the females are excellent sitters. They have, however, like those of other varieties, a gregarious tendency to lay their eggs in some other goose's nest. When one goes broody it is advisable to fence her in with a hurdle or straw bales and to provide food and water. Any well-meant assistance on the part of the owner is liable to result in serious injury. A blow or a bite hurts.

On balance, unless one has a pond or a stream, and low-lying land unsuitable for poultry, I doubt if they are worth the trouble. The old idea that they are as good as watchdogs has not been my experience. They are quarrelsome and vindictive with other species of poultry. Straying chickens are fair game. They cannot agree even with other varieties of water-fowl. I gave up keeping both when the gander killed the Muscovy drake.

Yet I find this latter variety fascinating. It is quite the easiest of all forms of poultry to keep, requiring literally no attention. They multiply exceedingly without any assistance—up to two dozen entrancing ducklings. How the tiny female can possibly cover so many eggs is a mystery. The nest is made of down in which the eggs are almost buried; when the mother does come off, completely so. She sits for at least five weeks almost anywhere, even up a tree or on top of the hayrick. From which you will gather that they can fly; and if annoyed they do. Unfortunately the flesh is dark and of no appeal to the poulterer. And the females weigh no more than a small hen. If however they can be persuaded to mate with other varieties of duck the offspring mules are uniformly enormous and delicious. To my mind Aylesburys are, by comparison, flavourless. From the caterer's point of view a Muscovy male is much better value. It is quite usual to carve a dozen or more portions. But to popularize them in this country— the Australians know better—it is necessary to dissuade the customers from the prejudice against their dark flesh.

To me this is quite incomprehensible. No one complains about partridges, pheasants, or guinea fowl. These two latter species incidentally are well worth considering. The time is rapidly approaching when chicken meat can pall. Pheasants are easy to rear; not so partridges. Guinea fowl are even easier—and noisier.

The females are prolific layers and, providing they are not disturbed reliable sitters. Unfortunately they are easy meat for foxes. Like geese they are not reliable sentries—they cry 'wolf' too often. And once can be fatal.

Peafowl? I have no personal experience. I am told they are difficult to rear as chicks and very prone to coccidiosis; my informant had not tried garlic. He admitted to having obtained £35 a pair. I must try a few hatching eggs.

Quail, the Japanese variety, are in the news. They are phenomenally productive, upwards of 300 eggs a year, most attractively marked, and sold hard-boiled on cocktail sticks for 5s. a dozen. Just how the carcases are prepared for table I do not know. Those I have seen have been kept intensively. I very much doubt if they would fit into my scheme of things.

Rabbits, perhaps; but not in battery cages. During the Hitler war I kept them like poultry, on the grass, moving the enclosures at the first indication of burrowing. Any that escaped were shot. My standard coop and run with board and wire netting floor served admirably for the does and young.

Guinea pigs, rats and mice are in demand by laboratories. They could bring in additional revenue. Goats too are at the time of writing quite profitable.

Whether these auxiliary enterprises are worth while depends on circumstances. One can so easily dissipate one's energies to the neglect of the main enterprise. On the other hand what began as a hobby could possibly be built up into a very profitable speciality.

Finally pigs. On the kind of establishment I am looking for there will be outbuildings, maybe a pigsty or two. If there is not, a loose-box or shed can be fitted with farrowing rails for a sow. She will serve a very useful purpose where hatching on a significant scale is contemplated. For there is bound to be debris whether one uses hens or incubators. And a sow is not fussy—she will save the cost of an incinerator, or the labour of digging. She will do that too, docks, bracken, couch grass. She will even prepare a rough seed bed. This if harrowed down in the autumn will give a useful sward of indigenous grasses.

If I obtain the kind of property I have in mind there will be ample room to store food, equipment, implements, crates, cartons, boxes and all the things that cannot be left outside. One needs too a repair shop, a garage and maybe an office. Should I fail in my quest and have to start from scratch, then I shall have to build. But I would prefer to make use of existing buildings. Quite apart from the fact that they do not depreciate to the same extent, they are usually better looking.

If the house is big enough I may even contemplate taking students, those about to retire for preference. There I shall hope to teach them the sort of things they will not learn from textbooks, and to make them familiar with honest to goodness poultry.

And how to keep their feet on the ground

INDEX